CLOCKS AND WATCHES
OF
NEW JERSEY

Early musical clock made by Isaac Brokaw of Elizabeth Town and Rahway
probably prior to 1802. The handsome
cabinet of cherry wood in Chippendale
style was made by Matthew Egerton, Sr.
of New Brunswick. This clock is a fine
example of the craftsmanship of New
Jersey clockmakers. Courtesy of Newark
Museum.

CLOCKS AND WATCHES

OF

NEW JERSEY

WILLIAM E. DROST

ENGINEERING PUBLISHERS

Elizabeth, New Jersey

Composed and printed by The Science Press, Inc., Subsidiary of The Printing Corporation of America

To the members of the New Jersey Chapter of the National Association of Watch and Clock Collectors, who helped make it possible, this book is gratefully dedicated.

Preface

CLOCKS AND WATCHES are among the most commonplace products of our time. They are made and sold by the millions each year. They are extensively used in the home, on the person, in business establishments, and in public places, to name just a few uses. *But it was not always so!*

Timekeeping was a serious problem to the people of colonial America, as it has continued to be to this day. At first clocks were imported from the mother countries of Europe. Of course, only the wealthy could afford the luxury of an imported watch or clock. These early time pieces were considered family heirlooms judging by their frequent and detailed mention in wills. It was inevitable that the construction of clocks be undertaken in the colonies. In a relatively short time, forty-six years, after the first permanent settlement in New Jersey at least one Jerseyman was earning his livelihood by making and selling clocks. Isaac Pearson of Burlington was undoubtedly the first clockmaker of New Jersey, and with the information at hand also in all of the American colonies.

Some of Pearson's clocks are in daily use now and they still keep good time after 250 years. Few other of man's mechanical contrivances can match this record.

Isaac Pearson was followed by many other clockmakers and watchmakers in New Jersey. It is their story that we try to give in this book.

Much in this book has been built upon the extensive work of other writers in this field. The works of Moore, Drepperd, Palmer, Britten, and others have been referenced in the text, to check and double check names, places and dates. As in any work of this nature there is repetition of names. The accomplishment here is that many clockmakers and watchmakers are treated in greater depth than heretofore had been done. Also, some workers not previously known are added. We know that future researchers will build upon our work and produce ever more complete histories of clockmaking and watchmaking in New Jersey. Also, we hope that readers will bring to our attention information not presently known to us.

From the inception of this work, we have been imbued with the thought that its value would depend largely upon the number and quality of illustrations. Some photographs were purchased from or given by museums, dealers, and individuals. Most of them, however, were made by the author especially for this book.

The reader will find great differences in the amount of information presented about the various clockmakers and watchmakers, and in the number and kind of illustrations of their work. This must in no way be construed that the author implies anything about the relative merits of their work. As anyone who has attempted historical research knows very well, the kind and amount of information obtained hinges very largely upon luck. Also, there is always a time limit beyond which one cannot go.

Acknowledgment

Many people have contributed to this book, and to them we offer a grateful "Thank you." These people include collectors, dealers, curators of museums and historical societies, and private owners. They provided a great deal of information and helped in obtaining many of the photographs.

Special thanks are due to the following persons and groups of people:

The many librarians who so cheerfully gave of their time and experience were found to be, if not guardian angels then surely guiding angels.

Mrs. A. T. Bauer who spent so much time and effort in preparing an illustrated talk on New Jersey clocks, and who made all of her material available for this book.

Richard Koles whose coaching in the use of the camera and whose darkroom "knowhow" made possible most of the illustrations.

Members of the New Jersey Chapter of The National Association of Watch and Clock Collectors who, singly and collectively, gave generously in material and moral support.

Edward J. Grassmann who permitted the intimate study and photography of his several New Jersey clocks.

Mrs. Caroline Baker whose many tidbits of information offered (and accepted) on the genealogy of the early clockmakers of New Jersey helped confirm or refute previous concepts.

Although their publications on American clocks are referred to in the footnotes and Bibliography, it is fitting that gratitude be expressed here to Carl Drepperd, Brooks Palmer, Carl Williams, and Margaret White. The help in their publications was invaluable in checking dates and locations, and in offering clues as to advertisements and other data.

William E. Drost

Elizabeth, New Jersey
September 1, 1966

Foreword

TIME is a *continuum* . . . it is invariable, without beginning and without end . . . it may be measured only by the aid of "reference points," and even then is anisotropic in its properties.

William E. Drost has established a "reference point" in time with this book, for now there is something "extant," embracing the span of 255 years, pertaining to and dwelling upon the arts and crafts of New Jersey, as related to and allied with horology.

A famous Princetonian, when speaking of his then newly developed Theory of Relativity, said that any project which required research had an heuristic value. This value applies to the material within these covers, for Mr. Drost has developed methods of investigation which lead us all to discover truths for ourselves. We should be thankful that he gives dates, names names, and provides abundant illustrations.

Certainly it is to be hoped that this will not be the last book to deal wholly with New Jersey clocks and clockmakers. To our knowledge it is the first, however, and is thus destined to occupy a unique niche.

The author is a modest man . . . we feel that it is only proper that any word from us should end with a repetition of his oft-expressed desire that should his book ever see the light of day, it be dedicated to students and collectors everywhere in general, and in New Jersey in particular.

EARL T. STRICKLER, F.B.H.I., Editor
BULLETIN of National Association
of Watch and Clock Collectors

Contents

Clockmaking in New Jersey

THE STATELY GRANDFATHER'S CLOCK is perhaps the greatest single evidence of fineness in the history of the arts and crafts of our nation. Few man-made products are handsomer, and even fewer have been more faithful in service. The gracious air they lend to even the finest surroundings is an attestation to their lasting beauty. Their service, continuous in some cases for more than 200 years, testifies to the ingenuity and skill of their makers.

Clocks of New Jersey take their place among the finest made in America and in the world. As an example, the clocks made by Aaron Dodd Crane, a New Jersey clockmaker of the last century, were known and admired the world over. A well known English horologist and author said, "Whilst in the early days of American clockmaking ideas and designs were copied largely from the English [who had in their turn copied from the Dutch], the final note is an example where the American horologist, Aaron Dodd Crane, led the world."*

The fineness of New Jersey clocks has gone unrecognized largely for the lack of telling the story of them. This book is an attempt to tell the story of the clocks and watches of New Jersey and of the men who made them.

The author may seem to digress occasionally from the hard and fast consideration of clocks and watches *per se*. Such digression is but an effort to provide a frame of reference so that the reader may be better able to visualize the entire story in relation to living and working conditions existing at the time the particular clocks and watches under discussion were made. Our justification for this digression may be found in the words of John Muir, the famous naturalist and explorer, "When we go to pick up any one thing, we find the whole rest of the world hitched to it." We shall forbear from telling *all* that we found "hitched" to each clock and watch we "pick up," and neither shall we strip it naked, leaving it bare of all human interest.

---

*H. Allan Lloyd, *Old Clocks*, p 167. Ernest Benn Ltd., London, 1958.

As in any book of this nature, many of the names mentioned are included in earlier works. Our contribution in this book is the addition of new information in greater depth than was heretofore given, plus the inclusion of newly researched material regarding unrecognized workers in the field.

There is a great difference in the amount of information offered here about the various makers, and the numbers and kinds of illustrations of their work. This must in no way be construed that the author implies by the large or small amount of material presented about each, the relative merit of each worker. As anyone who has attempted historical research will affirm, the kind and amount of information one can obtain hinges vastly upon luck. Also, there is a time limit beyond which one cannot go. An example of this will be found in the material on Aaron Dodd Crane. What is found herein on Crane is largely the result of an article written for the *Bulletin* of the National Association of Watch and Clock Collectors. (December 1956). The research involved in just this one instance required two and one-half years, and there are still some questions about Crane's work that are not fully answered. This is an explanation for the seeming discrepancy in the amount of information found regarding each of the craftsmen noted.

Greater understanding of the craft and industry of making clocks and watches and the men who made them may be reached if we know something of their environment—the Colony and the State of New Jersey.

No state has deeper roots in the history of our nation than does New Jersey. Verrazano's descriptions in 1524 and those of Henry Hudson in 1609 indicate that New Jersey's shores were the first sighted by the early European explorers. One of the thirteen Original Colonies, New Jersey had six signers of the Declaration of Independence. Much of the Revolutionary War was fought on its soil, making the materials for clockmaking —iron, brass, and lead—costly and hard to come by. The Provincial Congress of New Jersey thought so well of clockmaking that during the Revolution it passed an act providing Isaac Brokaw with 30 pounds of lead so that he could carry on his trade of clockmaking.

Small in size, but a giant in its impact and influence on the nation's industry and economy, New Jersey is a study in contrasts. It is only 166 miles long and a mere 32 miles across its narrow waist. Its northeastern area is considered by many atlases to be a part of the New England states, while its pointed toe is well south of the Mason and Dixon Line were it extended to the east. New Jersey is only 46th in size among the 50 states, yet it is eighth in population.

One of the oldest known clocks made in America is that of Isaac Pearson, who was making clocks in 1710 in Burlington, New Jersey. Who dares to say that Pearson, and the many craftsmen like him were not the forerunners of the scientists and technicians who make instruments for today's spacecraft.

The settlers of the early 1700's who were the early travelers between Boston, New York, and Philadelphia had looked upon the gently rolling hills of New Jersey with pleasure, and had then bought land and lived there. Still today New Jersey contains the suburbs of the great cities of New York and Philadelphia. The counties of Bergen, Essex, Hudson, Union and parts of Middlesex, Monmouth, Morris, Passaic, and Somerset are classed as of the metropolitan area of New York City. And although they are largely suburban in character, the counties of Camden, Burlington, and Gloucester are claimed as of the metropolitan area of Philadelphia.

In the compilation of names in this book, no time limit was set. Mention is made of the very earliest New Jersey clockmakers, Isaac Pearson and Aaron Miller, and also of a flourishing clock manufacturer of today, the Calculagraph Company in East Hanover.

In our usage of city directories and business directories we did set a dividing line with the years 1850–51. There seemed too great a prevalence for jewelry store owners and other merchants after this time who listed themselves as "watchmakers" or "clockmakers." There is an occasional exception to this rule, notably that of "P. Mason" whose label in his clock advertises his "Fancy Store."

Research in the city directories, in business directories, and in histories of various towns, revealed the mention of men as clockmakers whom the writer at first thought to omit. On further thought it was decided not to sit in judgment for the reader, simply because no tangible evidence of the "watchmaker" or "clockmaker" was known. It is altogether possible, even probable, that further search by others will bring to light a piece made by some listed here simply by name, location, and the time they were at work. An example justifying this decision is the instance of Oliver B. Marsh.

Marsh was noted in the writer's listing as early as 1954 and his name was about to be stricken as in no way being a clockmaker since the *Newark City Directory* listed him only as a jeweler. On receiving a catalog of the collection of Orville Hagans we noted a fine looking clock, "Made by Oliver B. Marsh, Newark, N. J." A beautiful clock made by Marsh is shown under his name later in this book.

The word "clockmaker" requires definition. There is a difference of opinion as to who should be called the clockmaker; the man who made the "works" or movement, or the man who made the case. The director of one of the fine museums in New Jersey holds firmly to the opinion that since the case is the larger and more obvious part, the man who made it should be called the clockmaker. Some private owners were found to hold this same opinion. Also, Phillipse Green included six names of cabinetmakers in his listing of New Jersey clockmakers.*

The writer cannot subscribe to this point of view and offers the following "argument." Suppose the completed case should stand by itself. It is *not* a clock. But hang the movement, with its dial, hands, pendulum, and weights, on the wall. *It is a clock.*

The case does protect the clock and when made by a skilled cabinet-maker, it is most certainly an embellishment to the clock and to its surroundings. We concede that a case can be made with greater skill and finer craftsmanship than the movement and to the owner may have the greater appeal because of its decorative value. This, however, does not make a clockmaker out of a cabinetmaker.

For the purpose of this book we differentiate between the two, and we call the man who made the case a cabinetmaker and the man who made the works the clockmaker. Those who, because of personal whim or fancy, concoct their own terminology as to "clockmaker," "watchmaker" or "casemaker" put themselves in the position of the only partially appreciative lady who cared less that she had a watch, than that she had an adornment on her wrist.

The president of a large watch company related this incident. His firm received back from a dealer a $5000 wrist watch which had been returned by a customer *several months* after she purchased it, with the explanation that she had just learned the watch did not go. The customer stated that she had shown it to a friend who casually attempted to wind it, but was not successful in doing so. The repair department of the watch company examined the watch in question only to find that the case contained no movement. A piece of cork was there instead. The president went on to explain that his firm customarily inserted movements in very high-priced watches only after the watches were ordered. In that way, the customer would be assured of getting a clean freshly oiled movement. In filling the order for the wrist watch in question, the order clerk had neglected to have a movement installed in it. This oversight was remedied, and a complete watch returned to the customer. However, had the customer never learned that her original "watch" could not be wound, she might have continued to enjoy wearing it for an indefinite period.

A similar hollow possession was noted in the instance of clocks. The piece was, on occasion, pointed out pridefully but with an apology that, "It isn't running now." Examination revealed that there was no clock,

---

*Phillipse Green, "Authentic List of Clockmakers Working in New Jersey," Antiques Section, *New York Sun*, October 14, 1949.

but just part of one. Having the case, in their minds, sufficed and they had a "clock."

It has been found that one cabinetmaker's name, John Scudder, appears on the dial of a clock. We know of no instance where a clockmaker affixed his name on the case. Joakim Hill, when he repaired a clock did write with white chalk in script on the inside of the door of the case his name and *repair* date.

In the appreciation of a clock lies the appreciation of the men who made it. This leads to the importance of a name. As the reputation of a clockmaker or a cabinetmaker grew, so has the value of his work grown. We are here chiefly concerned with the historical, mechanical, and aesthetic qualities of clocks. Wherever the word "value" is used it is in no way meant to imply the money value or price of today. Mention is made of the cost in a few instances (in the time it was made) of a clock, so we look for a name. The importance of knowing the name on the dial or in the case lies also in telling us where and when it was made. The desirability of owning one clock over another must lie with the owner or would-be owner. There would be little to choose between, let us say, an Isaac Brokaw clock and a Joseph Stillman clock from the aesthetic or mechanical points of view. Both are pleasing to look upon and both are still functional today, after some two hundred years. To the resident of Elizabeth the Brokaw, identified as being made in Elizabeth Town, would be the more valuable. To the native of Oldwick, the Stillman clock made in "New Germantown" (now Oldwick) would probably be the more desirable.

In considering the cost of the early watches and clocks the purchasing power of the dollar should be considered. The value of the dollar then as now was in direct proportion to the ease or difficulty with which it was obtained. The Table of Income, from the 1827 census of Paterson, is indicative of income of skilled and non-skilled labor. The word "indicative" is used advisedly for the table includes the labor of children which is not a factor in computing average individual income today.

In consideration for those to whom the money value of New Jersey clocks and watches is important, and those who may be interested in their impact on the economy within the state, the following information is offered.

We can appreciate the money values of the early watches and clocks only if we know and think of the relative value of the dollar of today and of yesteryear. The semi-skilled factory worker of today earns, on the average of $2.00 an hour or $80.00 for a forty-hour week. The skilled worker, the auto mechanic, the mason, the carpenter grosses as much as $200.00 for a forty-hour week and appreciably more when working overtime. As may be seen on the chart, compiled from the census of 1827, no worker in the machine shops in Paterson, made as much as $10 a week. Keep in mind

INCOME OF SKILLED AND UNSKILLED WORKERS IN 1827.

Kind of work	Men	Women	Boys & girls	Weekly payroll	Weekly pay per person
Candlestick factory	2		9	$15.00	$1.36
Turning shop	4			18.00	4.50
Wool carding machine	2			6.00	3.00
Turning shop	3			12.00	4.00
Cutlery and shears factory	3			24.00	8.00
Turning shop	14			60.00	4.28
Cotton factory	20	25	47	300.00	3.26
Cotton factory	9	7	34	125.00	2.50
Millwright and machine shop	11			66.00	6.00
Machine shop	10			50.00	5.00
Cotton and duck factory	12	52	29	275.00	2.95
Rolling mill and nail factory	25			160.00	6.40
Machine shop	68			650.00	9.50
Foundry	13			105.00	8.08
Cotton factory	2	5	26	75.00	2.27

Average per person, $4.74 per week.
From *Census of Paterson*, 1827 by Fisher.

too that the work week in 1827 was about sixty hours as compared with the forty hours of today.

Chauncy Jerome mentioned, when he was in New Jersey in 1812, that the clocks for which he made the cases sold for $40 complete. Jerome who made cases for the "works" being sold by the Yankee peddlers of Connecticut. (See "Jerome, Chauncy.") He was but nineteen years of age and had just finished his apprenticeship when he went to New Jersey to make the cases. It might be rightly assumed that his cases were not of the quality to bring the top prices of the day. The clocks of George Hollinshead were reported to have sold for $100.00 in the early 1800's.* Although no names of cabinetmakers have been found in the cases housing the clocks of George Hollinshead, most are obviously made by some fine craftsman of the day.

The quality of the case was then, as today, an important factor in the price of the whole clock.

The complexity of the money system of the nation in the late 1700's and early 1800's is indicated by the monies used at that time in New Jersey. So involved was it that in many advertisements offering items for sale in the newspapers of the day, notably the *Jersey-Journal* of 1780, frequently barter or exchange was preferred. We quote from a booklet *Tales of New*

---

*In a pamphlet of the First National Bank, Woodston, New Jersey. *Almanac and Yearbook 1864–1915.*

Jersey edited by Frank P. Townsend and published by New Jersey Bell Telephone Company.

"Anyone doing business in colonial New Jersey had to have his wits about him to know the value of the different coins passing through his hands. They came from many lands. There were English golden guineas, crowns and shillings; Portuguese crusadoes and "half-joes"; ecus from France; pillar pieces-of-eight, double-bits, bits and half-bits; Scotch four mark pieces; guilders and daaldars from Holland; pine tree shillings, ducatoons, rex dollars, cross dollars and dog dollars. Indian wampum circulated fairly freely. Too, New Jersey as a state coined its own coppers in 1786, 1787, and 1788. Popularly called 'horse head' cents and valued at 15 to the shilling, they were minted by Walter Mould, Thomas Goadsby, and Albion Cox, presumably at Morristown and Elizabeth."

Besides making clocks and instruments, Aaron Miller in Elizabeth applied his skill in metal work at making coins (privately) and was in a bit of trouble for counterfeiting. In addition to coins, there were the various kinds of paper money, looked upon with suspicion by many, that were printed by the several other colonies and sometimes by individual banks. As late as 1804 accounts were still kept in pounds, shillings, and pence rather than the new Federal decimal system.

Considering the income of the average individual of the day, the money value of watches was extremely high in colonial New Jersey. There were, of course, no watches being made anywhere in the country and those that were here were brought from Europe. Their worth might be judged by an advertisement in the *New Jersey Journal*, January 24, 1780:

"Lost, about the 6th or 8th instant, in or near Morris Town, a SILVER WATCH, with a steel chain and two brass keys, the seal green, a china face, broke near one edge, and cracked quite across with two or three cracks. Whoever delivers said watch to Mr. John Pain at Morris Town, shall receive One Hundred Dollars reward."

Watches were costly then and throughout the following century. The demand for them gave impetus to the establishment of factories in New England and New Jersey in the 1850's and later. The making of money, then as now, in many of these factories was the paramount interest and most factories failed because of the inferiority of their products.

The prices of clocks in New England, in the late 1700's and early 1800's were similar to those of New Jersey. Simon Willard advertised the prices of his clocks on his clock labels. One of his labels told the following:

"Simon Willard, at his Clock Dial in Roxbury Street, manufactures every kind of clock work, such as large clocks for steeples, made in the best manner and warranted, price with one dial, 500 dollars, with two dials, 600 dollars. Elegant eight day timepieces, price 30 dollars. Timepieces for Astronomical purposes, price 70 dollars. Timepieces for meeting houses to place before the gallery, with neat enameled dials, price 55 dollars. Chime clocks that will play six tunes, price 120 dollars. Perambulators are also made at the same place which can be affixed to any kind of wheel carriage, and will tell the miles and rods exact, price 15 dollars. Gentlemen who wish to purchase any kind of clocks are invited to call at said Willard's Clock Manufactory, where they will receive satisfactory evidence, that it is much cheaper to purchase new, than old and second hand clocks. He warrants all his work—and as he is ambitious to give satisfaction—he doubts not of receiving the public approbation and patronage."

The achievements of the early New Jersey clockmakers may be thought by some to be somewhat less than worthy because the maker was occupied also with other endeavors. They were also at the same time farmers, blacksmiths, tavernkeepers, silver and goldsmiths, merchants, and holders of public office. It is perhaps indicative of the quality of craftsmanship of some of the early New Jersey clockmakers that, "From the very beginning of the trade of Silversmithing until its decline about 1825, more than fifty percent of the silversmiths of New Jersey depended on the associated trades of clock and watch repairing as an important source of income."*

To deprecate one field of a man's total endeavors is to say that Samuel Morse's invention of telegraphy is less worthy because a painting of his hangs in the Metropolitan Museum of Art, and that Leonardo da Vinci's paintings are of a lesser quality because so much of his time was devoted to science and invention.

So we cannot, we must not, judge the quality of one product of a man's endeavors as being unworthy because he was successfully engaged in others, either at the same or other times. The manner in which the total man can ably express himself sometimes takes many avenues. That Joakim Hill was a farmer, that Aaron Lane was a silversmith, and that Aaron Miller also did blacksmithing should in no way detract from the consideration of their craftsmanship, or that of others, in the making of clocks.

The early clockmakers were, perhaps of necessity, men of diverse interests and capabilities. Clocks were costly in the early days even as good ones are expensive today. Not many could afford one, so customers being scarce, the clockmaker turned to other fields of endeavor. To augment his income he frequently worked at things other than making clocks, some related, some afield. Isaac Pearson, Aaron Miller and Aaron Lane were outstanding examples of the "wearing of many hats."

Whether the men, listed herein as clockmakers, were silversmiths, farmers, gunsmiths, jewelers, etc., who made clocks or whether they were clockmakers who worked in other fields we will make no attempt to say. A proper regard should be given the man, for whatever achievement, according to the quality of his work.

---

*Carl M. Williams, *Silversmiths of New Jersey 1700–1825*. George S. MacManus Company, Philadelphia, 1949.

Just as the cabinetmaker did not make the glass, the hinges, the locks and escutcheons in the case, so the clockmaker, especially after the 19th century, did not always compound the brass, cast the bells, make the dials or fashion the gut that suspended the weights. His work was that of obtaining the material, frequently preworked, then fashioning and fitting the parts, *making* of them—a clock.

Whether or not completed and pre-assembled clock movements were imported is not known to the writer. It is doubtful that they were. Of the many clocks examined there were, in the vast majority, those that bore some indication of the individual clockmaker, some much and some little. From about 1780 the majority of clock parts and dials were imported from England.

Elsewhere it has been reported that Aaron Miller advertised that he worked, "after the Dutch manner." None of the advertisements of Miller's that the writer has seen or learned about read otherwise than, "after the best manner." If the former were correct there would be the implication that Miller was Dutch or had been trained by a Dutch clockmaker. No evidence has been found that this might be so. To the contrary, the given names of the Miller family, the only clue the writer could find, were those found in English families.

The rarity in New Jersey, and for that matter anywhere in America, of clocks made "after the Dutch manner" is a reflection of the character of the early settlers.

The Dutch developed relatively little beyond primitive settlements during the years when New Jersey was part of New Netherlands. A sea-faring people, even the few settlements that were established were never far from the shore of the sea and often on the banks of a river. Interested chiefly in commerce, their speedy and plentiful ships furnished industrial products from the docks of Amsterdam. The few settlers who were lured to New Jersey during those early years had little occasion to manufacture anything beyond a few simple articles for their own domestic needs. The English settlers, having cause for discontent in their homeland, were those seeking to establish permanent homes. They brought with them all the requisites for permanancy including the tools and craftsmen to be as nearly self-sufficient as they might. Also, their reasons being greater, they came in far greater numbers than the peoples of any other country. Being in the majority, their customs, mores, and traditions prevailed and were dominant over those of others. Hence the style, design, and crafting of New Jersey clocks were predominantly English in character.

The years 1775 to 1800 would be the most accurate to choose as the division of time before which most clocks were largely hand crafted in America and after which most were importations of parts from England, fitted and assembled here, with the exception of the factory-made clocks of New England that were begun to be made in great quantities about 1820."

We might well pause here to consider that the greatest contribution the New England clockmakers made was the factory-made clock having interchangeable parts. Before this, only a family that was well off could own a clock at all. After Jerome, Terry, Seth Thomas, et al began their factories, almost any family could afford a clock and often two or three. Of course these inexpensive clocks were mostly shelf clocks many of which, during the years about 1790 to 1840 had wooden movements. Others were of weight-driven or spring-driven brass movements.

It is the intent of this book to offer information about the watches and clocks of New Jersey and a better understanding about them and the men who made them. While not a technical treatise, it is hoped that enough is included to interest the mechanically inclined. Such has been included to identify an individual's work or to distinguish one kind from another. Although, not a source for serious genealogical research, such has been included to more certainly identify the individual. It will also show, what may be of interest to some, the tendency of clockmaking and cabinet work to be a family affair, bringing about marriage and inter-marriage between members of various families, who had this mutual interest.

The reader will find throughout the following pages bits of information not dealing directly with watches and clocks and their makers. To the re-searcher seeking statistical and technical data these items might seem superfluous and interfering. We hope not too much. We repeat, that such asides and seeming extraneous things are offered believing they will serve as a kind of frame, by means of which the whole "picture" can be better seen.

An example of this is the table on page 6 devised from the Paterson census of 1827 which gives evidence of the value of the dollar at that time in terms of how many could be earned in a given week. Knowing this, the price of $40 to $100 for a clock becomes more meaningful. Not knowing this, and thinking in terms of income per week 100 to 200 of today's dol-lars, of the same class of working people, the reader is misled into think-ing that "clocks were cheap in those days."

The appreciation of the old clocks and watches, as in all objects of antiquity, lies in both the specific knowledge and in the "feeling" we have or acquire about them. The latter is not to be discounted or held in light esteem. Whatever proofs, age, maker's name, place of origin, associa-tion with persons of historical significance, or other evidence of authentic-ity—if the object does not stir the viewer, it has little value. Beliefs about these things are based on both knowledge and feeling.

Milton, in his lines from "Comus" considered the subject, thusly:

"Preach not me your musty rules
Ye drones that mold in idle cell,
The heart is wiser than the schools,
The senses also reason well."

In our search for truth, we look for certainty. We seldom find it. There are few things that are either black or white, almost all are simply different shades of gray. The names we find on the dials of clocks and/or on labels, which we sometimes trust too much, are sometimes found to be not quite what they seem. Too few have the simple, straightforward declaration on a label found in a New England shelf clock, owned by Mr. E. F. Tukey of Teaneck, New Jersey.

Patent Clock
Invented by Eli Terry
Movements made by Samuel Terry
Cased and finished by
Elisha Neale
New Hartford.

The casual reading of a label will sometimes mislead the observer. His eye is attracted by the boldest print and goes no further. An instance of this was noted, when a rather sophisticated collector was heard to remark, "The Crane clock is a New Jersey clock? I've always considered it a New York clock! The ones I've seen all have either a Fulton Street or a Cortlandt Street, New York City label in them!" To be sure, these labels did give these addresses, but information was available elsewhere that the clocks were *made* in Belleville, New Jersey. The labels simply gave the offices of distribution, of the entrepeneur who was involved in selling the clocks, in this instance J. R. Mills.

There are many clocks existing in New Jersey today that in style and fashion are of New Jersey make, but have no name to identify them. The names on their dials obliterated by too frequent and too careless cleaning are no longer visible or hardly so. Whether the labels sometimes found in the cases by the cabinetmakers have been removed or came loose and were disposed of over the years or perhaps never were applied is not known. It is known that a clock case with a cabinetmaker's name in it is a rare find. Here the "feeling" of design in the judgment of an experienced observer can usually, with a great degree of accuracy, determine who the cabinetmaker was and approximately when he made it. This is true also, to a lesser extent, in identifying the maker of the clock itself. The Brokaw clocks particularly have qualities indigenous to their makers. The clocks of about the 1790's and on are difficult to define as to maker or time due to their greater similarity, their parts more frequently being of factory make in England and supplied "in the rough" to be finished off by the clockmaker here, and then assembled into a working clock.

With but very rare exceptions, discounting the factory products of New England, the makers of clocks in America did not identify themselves on the movement or works. If they did identify themselves at all, their names are to be found on the dials, usually printed but sometimes engraved. The great number of movements, dials and dial parts, hands and intermediate plates imported from England and assembled here is a cause of concern as to which "maker," whose name appears on the dial, actually *made* the clock; created a design, cast the plates, cut the wheels and pinions, fashioned the dial and hands. To be able to distinguish with certainty the difference between a factory-made importation of parts and the work of a native craftsman would require great study. There have been found in New Jersey, clocks of various makes with qualities indigenous to that maker. These qualities were found in the hand crafted brass dials, different designs in the striking mechanism, the use of wooden winding drums sometimes sheathed with brass, the casting of lead weights.

In attempting to distinguish between those clocks which might be American made and those whose parts were imported, mostly from England, the design of the hands were found to be indicative. In the observation of these designs it was found that few if any could be thought to be only of American design and therefore a criterion that the whole clock was made here.

What is frequently called a Terry-type hand, with the diamond shaped cut outs, are found on English bracket clocks. Example, a Stephen Rimbault ca. 1780.

The most frequently found design in the minute hand is the type Wenham calls "squiggly."* For example, squiggly minute hands were used in the later clocks of Bridge Town of Isaac Brokaw. This design was also used in New England by Goddard, Taber, and the Willards. This is perhaps the most frequently used design on tall clocks beginning in about 1780. The style used by Aaron Miller and the earlier Hollinsheads on their minute hands—was the longer straight line emanating from a relatively short bit of iron filagree near its point of mounting.

Hour hand designs varied more in the piercing of their broad pear shape than in the character of the whole.

---

*Edward Wenham, "Old Clocks for Modern Use." G. Bell & Sons Ltd., London, 1951.

Clockmakers of New Jersey

1710–1966

AMERICAN CALENDAR CLOCK COMPANY, *Newark*. Advertised in the Newark City Directory of 1858, "American Calendar Clock Company, Railroad Avenue, Opposite the Depot."

BAILEY, GAMALIEL, *Mount Holly*. Known to have training and experience in repairing. No clocks are known to have been made by him. His shop was on Main Street near Mill Street, 1807–1820.

BONNEL, JACOB, *Chatham*. Born, May 1767. Died in 1841. His will was dated February 17, 1837. He was a third-generation Bonnel, son of Captain Nathaniel Bonnel, and grandson of Nathaniel Bonnel. He married Margaret Crane. Only one of his clocks is known and it is illustrated in the accompanying photograph. Upon examination this clock was found to have a movement that is an exact counterpart of the Isaac Brokaw early clocks. The dial is of brass, hand hammered quite thin, ornamented with engraving and with the inscription in the lunette, "Jacob Bonnel, Chatham, 1793." Although the movement of this clock, and possibly also the dial, may have been obtained from Brokaw (who was born and did his early clockmaking in the Chatham area of Hillsborough), Bonnel was a clockmaker. This is borne out by the inventory of his possessions made after his death, "6 unfinished clocks and box, 1 vise, stakes, clockmakers tools, 1 musick clock." Bonnel was mentioned as a clockmaker in John Littel's, "*Family Records or Genealogies of the First Settlers of Passaic Valley,*" 1851.

BRADLEY, L., *Jersey City*. Patent No. 95,316, September 28, 1869, Electric Clock.

Clock of Jacob Bonnel. The movement
of this clock is indistinguishable from
those made by Isaac Brokaw. The movement may well have been purchased from
Brokaw and installed in the cabinet by
Bonnel. Owned by Edwin Huff, Jr. of
Neshanic Station.

Dial of the Bonnel clock. It is of quite thin brass and engraved.

BROKAW, AARON, *Rahway*. Born in Hillsborough Township, Somerset County, June 23, 1768. Died in Rahway, December 18, 1853. The dials of his clocks were inscribed both "Bridge Town" (the old name for part of Rahway) and "Rahway, E. J." The E. J. was for East Jersey.

Aaron was the second son of Isaac Brokaw. Even as his father's work showed the influence of *his* teacher Aaron Miller, so does Aaron Brokaw's clock show that he learned his trade from his father. One of Aaron Brokaw's clocks was found to be almost identical with some of his father's work. Of the several clocks known to be of Aaron Brokaw, one has a dial employing the "Moon Phase" mechanism. Others use the English dials, but they are of the painted iron type using the "Osborne" false or intermediate plate, and also the toothed calendar wheel marked "Osborne Manufactory, Birmingham." Elmer T. Hutchinson, in his excellent article on the Brokaws (*Proceedings of the New Jersey Historical Society*, July 1954) says, "A direct descendant has stated that Aaron acquired all of his father's tools, among which was an ingenious gear cutting machine that Isaac had devised early in his career."

BROKAW, ISAAC, *Rahway*, *Bridge Town*, and *Elizabeth Town*. Born in 1746 in Hillsborough Township. Died September 1826 in Rahway. Brokaw was apprenticed in about 1760 to Aaron Miller of Elizabeth Town. He married Miller's daughter Elizabeth in 1766. The relationship between Isaac and his teacher and father-in-law was apparently a close one for in his will Aaron Miller left "(to my) son Cornelius and my son-in-law Isaac Brokaw my clockmaking tools."

About 1760 to 1765 Brokaw returned to Hillsborough Township where he set up in the clockmaking business. He was active there, although none of his clocks have been found with a Hillsborough Township identification on it. His work in Hillsborough was thought to be important as is proven by an "Act of Congress." In the minutes of the Provincial Congress and the Council of Safety of the State of New Jersey it is recorded, "The Province Congress in 1776 ordered that the Committee of the Township of Hillsborough, in the County of Somerset, do leave in the hands of Mr. Isaac Brokaw, clockmaker, thirty pounds weight of lead, he having represented to the convention that he could not carry on his trade without such quantity, Saturday, July 27 (1776)."

Both Aaron Miller and his son Cornelius died in 1779 leaving Elizabeth Town without a clockmaker. Brokaw promptly returned to Elizabeth Town and set up his clockmaking business on the premises where he had learned his trade. He was active here until 1788–89

Aaron Brokaw clock owned by Edward J.
Grassmann of Elizabeth.

Dial and hood of the Aaron Brokaw clock.

Movement of the Aaron Brokaw clock. The simple and efficient
striking mechanism is typical of the clocks made by Aaron Brokaw.

Isaac Brokaw musical clock in a cabinet of cherry in Chippendale style made by Matthew Egerton, Sr. Collection of the Newark Museum.

Movement of the Isaac Brokaw musical clock. The propellor-like wind vane is to control the speed at which the
musical part of the clock operates.

One of Isaac Brokaw's later clocks.
Owned by Miss May Kirtland of East
Orange.

Detail of the later clock of Isaac Brokaw showing the odd-shaped cutout in the back plate. Did Brokaw need a small piece of brass?

An early Isaac Brokaw clock. No location or date is shown on the dial. Owned by Edward J. Grassmann of Elizabeth.

Dial of the early Isaac Brokaw clock showing that the spandrels are missing. The holes through which they would have been fastened are neatly plugged indicating that the clock might have been made with deference to the simple taste of a Quaker.

Movement of the early Isaac Brokaw clock has an ornamental bell that is unusual and might possibly be a replacement for the original. Note that the corner of the back plate has been cut off.

when he moved to Bridge Town (now part of Rahway) leaving his oldest son John in charge of the shop in Elizabeth Town. Brokaw continued making clocks in Bridge Town until 1816 when he turned over the business to his son Aaron.

Mention has been made of the closeness between Isaac Brokaw and his teacher and father-in-law, Aaron Miller. How very close is seen in the naming of Isaac's sons.

It was the custom in fruitful marriages of the early days in New Jersey, as elsewhere, to name the first-born male after the grandfather on the paternal side and the second-born male after the grandfather on the maternal side. This custom was followed by Isaac Brokaw in naming his sons, John and Aaron, and doing so out of regard for and deference to his father-in-law, Aaron Miller.

It may have been, though nothing certain is now known, that Isaac Brokaw's immediate family was of the Dutch Reformed church, for it is in that church where records of the Brokaw family can be found. The name, according to these records was variously spelled Broka, Broeka, Brocarde, Broekaess and Broucard. The first known was a Bourgon Broucard, a Hugenot refugee who settled in Bushwick, Long Island in 1675. Four sons settled around Raritan, Somerset County. Isaac's parents were Jan and Marytee Broeka.

Because of the desirability of dating Isaac Brokaw's clocks, the involvement of the names of localities must be considered. Elizabeth Town originally comprised all of the present Union County and some areas beyond. These included Woodbridge and an area given over to Newark. Woodbridge in 1701 was known as Bridge Town or Lower Rahway. In 1822 Bridge Town became a part of Rahway. Elizabeth Town did not become Elizabeth until 1863.

It is not determined whether Brokaw did a lot of moving around, as indicated by the different localities on his dials, or whether the localities changed their names "under him," as it were.

The very earliest of Isaac Brokaw's clocks had only his name on them, no locality. They were probably made in Hillsborough Township, just after he finished his apprenticeship, married and "went out on his own." The early clocks of his that were first identified with a locality were of Elizabeth Town, and his latest of Rahway. The clocks inscribed "Rahway" were his latest ones and were using the English import kind of parts. These included the "Osborne" dials, false plates, and calendar dials. On these is the Moon Phase in the lunette.

On examining the clocks of Isaac Brokaw, the early ones show every evidence of handcrafting, even to the hand hammering of the brass dials. He copied the craft in general from Aaron Miller, both

Another early clock of Isaac Brokaw made in Elizabeth Town in 1788. Owned by Edward J. Grassmann of Elizabeth.

Dial of the early Isaac Brokaw clock.

One of the later clocks made by Isaac Brokaw. Owned by Edward J. Grassmann of Elizabeth.

Dial of the later Isaac Brokaw clock shown in the previous illustration. The stylized hands, the iron painted dial, the "Osborne" false plate, and character of the movement all indicate the use of parts imported from England, and finished and fitted in New Jersey.

Early clock of Isaac Brokaw in a cabinet
quite different from those usually containing his clocks. Owned by John
Albertine of South Bound Brook.

Dial of the early Isaac Brokaw clock shown in the previous illustration.

An early transitional clock of Isaac Brokaw. The hands, dial, and false plate ("Wilson") are English. The movement is Brokaw's. The outstanding feature, aside from the fine quality, is the platform made for the cabinet to stand upon. The well, built within the platform permits the weights to have their maximum drop, while the walls of the well, when within the case of the cabinet, afford a sealing off against dust rising upward to contaminate the movement. Courtesy of Israel Sack, Inc. of New York.

in design and in the manner of making. This obedience to the instruction and example of Miller is revealed in a peculiarity seen in some clocks of both. This peculiarity is a piece of the back plate missing! Almost always, when it is found, the upper right hand corner has been cut off. In one instance an irregular piece was found cut out of the center right hand edge of the back plate. (See photographs of Miller and Isaac Brokaw movements.) Why was this done? It is the writer's opinion that in his disposition to conserve or simply obtain brass for a small part—brass was hard to come by in these days—Aaron Miller had simply cut off a piece where it would not be missed, at least as far as function was concerned. Why do Isaac Brokaw's clocks sometimes show this same characteristic? Well . . . didn't he learn the trade (and the tricks of the trade) from Aaron Miller?

The life of Isaac Brokaw, as his work evidences, spanned that era of transition in clockmaking in New Jersey and in America from the entire making of a clock by the maximum of craftsmanship, to the later finishing off and assemblage of parts factory-made in England.

Some of the cases for Brokaw's clocks are known to have been made by Rosett & Mulford, John Scudder, Mathew Egerton, Jr., and Richardson Gray.

Both Isaac Brokaw and his son Aaron lie in the cemetery of the First Presbyterian Church in Rahway.

AN ISAAC BROKAW CLOCK—A PHOTOGRAPHIC ESSAY

We have attempted to show as many photographs as possible in this book. The purpose being to give evidence, at all, of the various makers and to provide the knowledge of the kind of work they did. In many instances more than one photograph is shown to satisfy the interest of those who think of a clock as a piece of furniture, and also to give more than perfunctory consideration to those who think of a clock as a mechanism.

In this instance, of this particular Isaac Brokaw clock, we offer as much detail as we know how. This particular specimen was chosen for good reasons. It was at hand, it is old by American standards (180 years), the case is above average in the quality of cabinet work and style, the dial and movement are hand-crafted throughout. It is and, in our opinion, deserves to be, representative of New Jersey craftsmanship and style in the making of clocks.

The accompanying photograph shows the clock as a whole. The case is of cherry wood expertly fashioned. Unusual is the design of the hood in that the scrolls of the broken arch continue on through to the back of the hood. Although this has been seen on some few pieces of furniture, the

A clock most typical of Isaac Brokaw's work. Details of this clock are shown in the following photographs.

Dial of the typical Isaac Brokaw clock shown in the previous illustration.

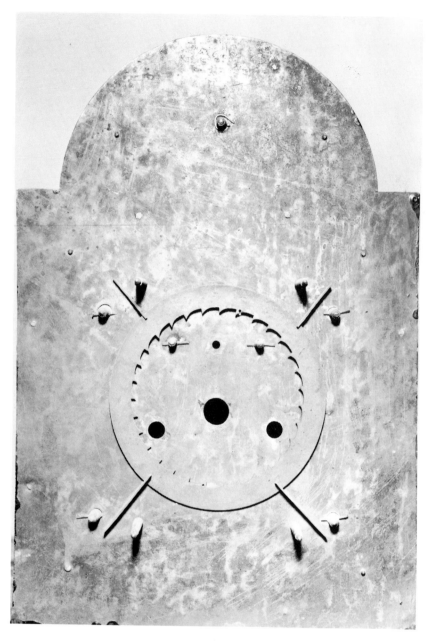

Rear of the typical Isaac Brokaw dial.

Front view of the movement of the typical Isaac Brokaw clock.

Rear view of the movement of the typical Isaac Brokaw clock.

Right side of the movement of the typical Isaac Brokaw clock.

Left side of the movement of the typical Isaac Brokaw clock.

writer has not seen this on any other clock case. The terminal part of the scrolls are made of solid wood and extending as they do the depth of the hood help to make the hood exceptionally heavy, about 35 to 40 pounds. The finials are of wood in the ball-and-spike design. Unfortunately, but as is most common, the cabinetmaker is unknown.

Inside the case was found, tacked to the back, a prescription blank of Dr. Edward Phelan, M.D., of 18 South Street, Newark, New Jersey. On this was written, "Bought of Isaac Brokaw, in 1785, by Elihu Bond of Lyons Farms. Five pounds for the clock and five pounds for the works. Was in the Bond family until 1917, when it became the property of Dr. Edward Phelan of Newark."

The dial is of brass hand hammered to a thinness that was found unusual as compared to those of other makers (about 1/16 of an inch), but common in most of the Brokaw clocks, in Isaac's as well as in those of his sons Aaron and John. The spandrels are of pewter as are the chapter rings, both hour and seconds, and also the medallion in the lunette of the dial, upon which is engraved "Isaac Brokaw, Eliz. Town, 1785."

The rear of the dial shows the hammer marks. Of the pinned studs extending through the dial, the two innermost within the toothed calendar ring hold the seconds chapter ring. The four outermost hold the hour chapter ring. The single stud, in the lunette portion of the dial, originates from the medallion on front. The four studs located so as to form an upright rectangle are the "feet" by which the dial is attached to the front plate of the movement. The 1-1/4-inch long slender pieces set at a 45-degree angle are slotted at the ends to retain and guide the calendar ring.

The front view of the movement shows the "streak of lightning" shaped lifting lever for the strike, and also the lack of relatively complicated strike mechanism as in the "rack and snail" types. Aaron Miller used this simple strike design as did Isaac Brokaw's sons, John and Aaron.

The rear view of the movement gives evidence of Brokaw's disposition to occasionally slice off this particular corner of the back plate. Pit marks tell that the plates were cast. The projection on the right side, seen over the edge of the plate and under the bell, is the edge of the wind vane. In this clock it is oddly thick and by comparison, very heavy.

The left side of the movement shows the wood winding drums with the visible gouging caused by the metal cables. The original cables were almost surely of gut, and would not produce the abrasive wear that the replacement cables are causing. The early makers knew, what apparently some of our modern repairmen have yet to learn, that it's just good mechanical sense to have wood work against wood and metal against metal and not mix the two. The same good sense applies to the use of the softer gut or cord for the suspension of weights.

Noteworthy are the gently tapered pillars between the plates. These are of iron, not the usual brass found in later clocks. The later brass pillars had heavier shoulders butting against the plates and were, particularly the imported English type, more elaborately machined and had a heavy "bead" in the center.

The left side view of the movement shows the count wheel typical of Miller and the Brokaws. It is solidly mounted just before and onto the main wheel of the strike train. Although the count wheel was used for a great many years before, to the best of the writer's knowledge, it was always mounted (when used) outside the back plate. Unless and until other knowledge comes to the fore we must assume that this is a design indigenous to Aaron Miller and learned about and used by the Brokaws. Note, too, that the striking hammer is mounted fairly in the center between the two plates. Admitting that this is no criterion, it must be here stated that this was found on New Jersey clocks that were indisputably fashioned in New Jersey. Those that had the characteristics of parts made in England were so designed that the hammer was found snugly near the back plate.

BROKAW, CORNELIUS, *Rahway*.   Born in Hillsborough Township, September 27, 1772. Died in Plainfield, April 9, 1857. Youngest son of Isaac, he repaired clocks and either alone or with his brother Aaron, made clocks. Several clocks bearing his name reported. Moved to Plainfield about 1846. No clocks known to the writer of that location.

BROKAW, JOHN, *Elizabeth Town, Woodbridge, Bridge Town*.   Born in Hillsborough Township, 1767, the oldest son of Isaac Brokaw. Married in 1788 to Rebecca Miller, daughter of Andrew and Sarah (Ross) Miller of Westfield. A sister of Rebecca was married to Captain John Scudder, a cabinetmaker whose cases housed several New Jersey clockmakers work, including that of John Brokaw. John worked with his father in the Elizabeth Town shop and took over the business there in 1788 or 1789. Upon his father's retirement in 1816, John moved to Rahway where he continued to make and repair clocks. The writer has seen six of his clocks. One, not seen, was described in the magazine *Antiques* (May 1944, p 270) which mentions a clock with the inscription "John Brokaw, E. Town." Also, inside the case is scratched the date "May 5, 1803" below which are the initials, "J. B." This might have been the date the clock was made or sold.

Note: Much of the material on the Brokaws was obtained from the excellent article, "Isaac Brokaw, New Jersey Clockmaker" by Elmer

Clock of John Brokaw of Bridge Town.
The case is of mahogany inlaid with
satinwood and attributed to Matthew
Egerton, Jr. Collection of the Newark
Museum.

Clock of John Brokaw of Elizabeth Town
made in the late 1700's or early 1800's.
Owned by the State of New Jersey and
located in Boxwood Hall in Elizabeth.

Dial of the John Brokaw clock shown in the previous photograph.
Noteworthy is the extreme thinness of the hand-hammered brass
of the dial, so thin that the dial has begun to tear at the edges.

Movement of the John Brokaw clock. The winding drums are of wood, characteristic of almost all Brokaw movements. The pulleys are also of wood.

T. Hutchinson published in the *Proceedings of the New Jersey Historical Society,* July 1954. The writer is grateful for the permission granted to use the material from the article.

BRUEN, CALEB, *Newark.* Prior to 1800, a cabinetmaker.

BRUEN, THOMAS, *Newark,* 1820's, a cabinetmaker. Son of Caleb.

BUDD, BEN, *Mount Holly.* Obviously *not* a maker of clocks or watches, his label dated May 24, 1907 found in a Morgan Hollinshead clock was intriguing to the writer. It is offered here for such interest and amusement as might be found. The "Mechanical Expert's" opinion of "yankee wooden-work clocks" (by failing to dignify their mention in capitals as he did the French) is worth a chuckle.

BUDD, JOSEPH, *Mount Holly* and *Pemberton, New Jersey* and *Hamilton, Ohio.* In New Jersey from 1814 to 1830. Listed as a clockmaker in Mount Holly by De Cou. An advertisement of Budd's in the *New Jersey Mirror and Burlington County Advertiser* of November 22, 1820 noted that he commenced business as a clock and watchmaker, "opposite James Wilson's Tavern in New Mills" (now Pemberton). Mr. James Gibbs, in his research of Ohio clockmakers, observed and sent on the following, "About 1833 Joseph Budd produced at least a few clocks in Hamilton (Ohio), one of which is still in use by one of the pioneer families of Hamilton. After many hours of research we find that this indeed is the same Joseph Budd, formerly of Mount Holly, New Jersey who came to Hamilton in the early 1830's. He is listed as a silversmith and clockmaker in the Hamilton, Ohio records found for 1833."

BULL, JAMES P., *Newark.* In *Newark Directories* 1850–1857.

BURGI, FREDERICK, *Bound Brook and Trenton.* Advertised in the *New York Mercury* May 19, 1766. Was in partnership with William Hurtin operating as "Hurtin & Burgi." William Hurtin was a silversmith and Burgi may have been a repairer only. He was employed as a clockmaker by another silversmith, John Fitch about 1774–75; also in Trenton.

BURNET, SMITH, *Newark.* Born 1770, died 1830. Advertisements found were dated December 10, 1793, December 18, 1793. In July 1794 he advertised for a "journeyman to the clock and silversmiths business." His shop in 1793 was "opposite Gifford's Tavern" then on Broad

BEN BUDD,

MECHANICAL EXPERT,

MOUNT HOLLY, N. J.

Clocks, Organs, Sewing Machines, &c,
Cleaned and Repaired, at your house anywhere in Burlington County, Trenton,
Camden, and Philadelphia, for the following charges: For cleaning

Common Mantel or Wall Clocks, . $1.00
New Style Black or China Case, . . $1.25
Old Fashion "Grandfather," or French $2.00
Sewing Machines $2.00.   Organs, $3.00

All work done in a first-class manner, having
had twenty years experience. A specialty made
of fine French and yankee wooden-work
clocks, Also of old fashion "Grandfather"
clocks, having five hundred of them in my
care to keep in order.

Orders will receive attention if sent by
mail, write what you want done and
where you live, on a postal card or letter,
and mail it to my address as given above.
All work warranted.   This clock cleaned for

Date,

An interesting card of Ben Budd found tacked inside the case of a
Morgan Hollinshead clock.

Street near Market, advertisements were repeated for this address January 1–8–15–22–29, all in *Wood's Gazette* in 1794. Carl Williams in his book, "Silversmiths of New Jersey" stated, "The inventory of Smith Burnet's estate, as well as numerous advertisements, indicate that he was also a practical clockmaker. When he died, two unfinished clocks comprised part of his personal property." There is mention of Smith Burnet as a private in September 9, 1794—three-month enlistment—in Captain Thomas Ward's Troop of Light Dragoons, First Regiment of Cavalry serving in the Pennsylvania Insurrection of 1794, from Essex County. (From, *Officers and Men of New Jersey in Wars 1791–1815*.)

BURROWS AND HOWELL, *Elizabeth Town*. Cabinetmakers? They bought a business from Richardson Gray in June 1803. Although they are listed elsewhere as cabinetmakers, there is little evidence found to substantiate that. All advertisements the writer found indicated that only merchandise was sold on the premises, "calico and yard goods, mirrors, whiskey by the barrel, shingles of superior quality." In an advertisement of January 10, 1804 in the *Jersey Journal*, there was also mention that "S. Burrows carries on the tayloring (sic) Business." Advertisements of Burrows and Howell were noted in the *Jersey Journal* from 1804 to 1808.

CALCULAGRAPH COMPANY, *New York City*, 1888; *Harrison, New Jersey*, 1910; and *East Hanover, New Jersey*, 1960. The same Henry Abbott, noted in the watch industry in the late 1800's for his inventions of stem winding conversion of key wind watches (see Abbott in the watch section), created the Calculagraph clock.

On the day of the blizzard of 1888 at 4 Maiden Lane in New York City, in Abbott's own words, "The Calculagraph was born." The clock was manufactured variously at 9, 11, and 13 Maiden Lane. In 1910, larger facilities being needed, the factory moved to Harrison, New Jersey. This move may have been, in part, due to Abbott's almost lifelong residence at 66 South Clinton Street, East Orange. In 1960 the factory had again outgrown its premises and moved to its present location in East Hanover, New Jersey.

The Calculagraph is a special kind of clock. It has the usual hands and face. It prints the time of day as any other time recorder, but then the indigenous qualities of this clock take over, and we find that it also calculates and prints elapsed time in hours and minutes or in minutes and seconds. Then, if required, it will also calculate the value of the elapsed time in dollars and cents or even in foreign currency.

Modern factory of the Calculagraph Company in East Hanover.

The first place on the Lane dug out after the BLIZZARD.

New York, March 12th, 1888.

Birthplace of the Calculagraph Company in New York City on the day of the blizzard of 1888.

Many models of the Calculagraph clock have been made to suit the particular need of the user. The Calculagraph has been used by livery stables, renters of bicycles, billiard parlors, telephone companies and factories who have found the timing of operational procedures expedient.

The Calculagraph factory is today operated by William C. Moodie, Sr. Mr. Moodie began working for Henry Abbott in 1925, when he was engaged as chief engineer. Besides five patents of his own, relating to the Calculagraph, Mr. Moodie has over the years contributed other devices, improvements, and changes that have gone directly into the manufacture of the clock.

The early movements of the Calculagraph clock were all spring powered. About 1925 these were gradually replaced with an electrical model driven by a synchronous motor.

The present Calculagraph factory is a fine modern combination of offices and shops. Although the company manufactures another device, one to measure very fine thermal differences, the time measuring device, the clock, is still the main product.

CALLIS, JAMES, *Flemington.* Clock and watchmaker, 1850–51. *Kirkbride's Directory.*

CANNON, WILLIAM, *Burlington.* About 1740–50. Worked in Philadelphia in the 1720's and moved to Burlington, New Jersey. Died there in 1753.

In the records of *New Jersey Marriages Before 1800,* it is noted that "William Cannon of Philadelphia was married to Sarah Jackson of Philadelphia August 19, 1738." There were at this time an Arthur and a Richard Cannon in Philadelphia. A logical deduction would be that William Cannon apprenticed in Philadelphia and having his family in Burlington, returned there to be married to the girl he met in Philadelphia. Cannon apparently remained and carried on with his clockmaking trade in Burlington. In the *New Jersey Archives of Wills* is noted, "October 4th 1753, William Cannon, of Burlington City, Clockmaker, intestate. Bond of Joseph Hollinshead, Esq. Administrator...."

CARPENTER, SAMUEL, *South Trenton.* 1850–51. Listed in *Kirkbride's Directory* as "Clock and Watch Maker," Bloomsbury Street.

CHASE, JOHN F., *Newark,* 1851–54. Listed in *Newark City Directory.*

CHASE, W. D., *Hackensack*. Patent No. 337,377, March 9, 1886 for clock. Patent No. 373,441, November 22, 1887 for Clock.

CHRISTY, JOHN A., *Trenton*. In the *New Jersey Gazette* of Trenton for April 10, 1786 the following advertisement was noted; "If John A. Christy, Silversmith, Watch and Clock Maker, son of William Christy, merchant of London, will apply to the printer of this paper, he will receive intelligence which will be very pleasing to him."

CLARK, DAVID A., *Trenton*. Listed in Kirkbride's Directory, 1850–1851 as "Clark, David A., Clock and Watch Maker, 3 East State Street." The spelling of the name and a possible error in location is indicated by the only other evidence found of "Clark, David A." The watch paper, in the watchmakers section, gives a different spelling of the name and a different location.

CLARKE, C. L., *East Orange*. Patent 347,572, 1886. For Electric Clock System. Patent 367,960, 1887. For Electric Clock System.

CLEVELAND, BENJAMIN NORTON, *Newark*. Born 1767 and died 1837. In the *Cleveland Genealogy* Benjamin Norton Cleveland is mentioned as "From Southold [Long Island] about 1790 to Newark where he was a real estate owner and well known. He was a manufacturer of clocks and watches and silverware and carried on the business many years. His store was on the east side of Broad Street about 4 doors North of Market Street. A Tall Regulator clock with B. Cleveland New Ark painted on the dial, now stands [1899] in the hall of the homestead of N. H. Cleveland, Southold, L.I."

Cleveland advertised in "*Wood's Gazette*" in Newark, October 4, 1792, "The subscriber begs leave to inform his friends and the public, that he now carries on the Clock and Watch Making business in all its various branches in Newark opposite the court house. He has now in his employ a workman who has been regularly brought up to the above business in the first shop in the city of Edinburgh and has been employed in the first shops in the city of New York—at Persall and Embree's for many years past.

"He likewise carries on the GOLD & SILVER smith business. Those who may please to favor him with their commands, may depend on being faithfully served at the shortest notice and their favors thankfully accepted by their humble servant. Benjamin Cleveland."

In the *Newark City Directory* for 1835–36, Cleveland's name was misspelled and entered as "Cleavland." His address was given as 327 Broad Street.

Clock made by Benjamin Cleveland.
Owned by Mr. and Mrs. Carl Dalrymple
of Dover.

Dial of the Benjamin Cleveland clock.

COOPER, ISAAC MICKLE, *Trenton*. Was with Ben. Clark in Philadelphia in the early 1800's.

CONNOR, J., *Jersey City*. Patent No. 155,224, 1874, for Lifting Hooks for Striking Clocks. Patent No. 210,755, 1878, for Lockwork Attachment for Clocks.

COPPUCK, GEORGE WASHINGTON, *Mount Holly*. Born February 7, 1804, died February 21, 1882. Son of James Coppuck and Elizabeth (Knight) of Mount Holly. Had his shop on Mill Street and advertised in the *Mount Holly Mirror*, listing jewelry and silver spoons for sale. His clock dials are inscribed, "G. W. Coppuck Mount Holly."

"CORNU" CLOCK. First glance will show that the "Cornu" clock is not of New Jersey or even American origin. Its mention here is because of its obvious artistic and horological importance and because it exists in New Jersey. The clock is in the possession of the Passaic County Historical Society and is located in the museum at Lambert Castle in Paterson, New Jersey. It stands on the main floor just to the right of the entrance. Its size and splendor commands immediate attention as one first glances about.

Towering 13 feet 6 inches high, the clock is made up of four sections: A pedestal of apparent marble measuring 35 inches deep by $28\frac{1}{2}$ inches wide, the base of onyx, the case of onyx, and the statue.

The statue is of an upright draped female form holding aloft a torch. From the base of the torch is suspended the rotary pendulum. The pendulum ball is a rich blue liberally spangled with gilt stars. The statue is bronze. Cast into the base of the statue is the name, "A. Carrier" (full name was Albert Enrest Carrier-Belleuse). Carrier was a French sculptor, born in Anizy-le-Chateau in 1824. He was a pupil of David d'Angers and while studying earned his living making models for the manufacturers of bronzes. He won notice with his first piece of sculpture, a marble statue representing "The Death of General Desaix" in 1859. "The Messiah," a group in St. Vincent de Paul's church in Rome, won Carrier a medal of honor in 1867. Other works of Carrier's were, "Angelica," "Madonna and Child," "Sleeping Hebe," "Forsaken Psyche." He was honored for his particularly true-to-life busts of Gauthier, Alout, and Renan. In his later life Carrier became director of the Art Department of the world renowned porcelain works, "a Sevres." He died in Paris in 1887.

A second name on the clock, the one by which the clock is most frequently identified is Eugene Cornu. It is found on the upper left side of the case as "E. Cornu" and engraved on a metal plate located

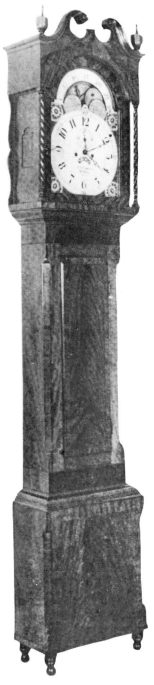

Clock of George Washington Coppuck.
From Carl Williams, "*Silversmiths of New
Jersey.*" Courtesy of George S. Mac-
Manus Company of Philadelphia.

"Cornu" clock located in the museum at
Lambert Castle in Paterson. The overall height is $13\frac{1}{2}$ feet.

at the lower right hand side of the clock movement, within the chapter ring that designates the hours. Here the engraving reads, "Eugene Cornu, Boulevard des Italiens 24, Paris." The third name is engraved below that of Cornu's on the metal plate. It is, "E. Fared, hologer."

It is not unreasonable to assume that Carrier made the statue, Fared made the movement, and Cornu perhaps made the case but did correlate the whole.

The front of the clock has two dials. The upper dial indicates the hours of the day, the lower dial the days of the week and of the month, and also moon phases. On the left side of the case is the dial of a thermometer in Centigrade degrees. On the right side of the case is another thermometer in Fahrenheit degrees. On the rear of the case are two dials, the upper that of a barometer, the lower has a manually operated indicator which computes the time of day of various geographic locations as compared with Paris as a reference point.

A short account of the Cornu clock in the *Bulletin* of the Passaic County Historical Society of December, 1958 stated that the Cornu clock was on exhibit at the Paris Exposition in 1867. In this same account is related how the clock was acquired by Mr. Lambert, "One of New York's great art dealers while scouting for art in Chicago, saw the clock (there) and purchased it. He took it back to New York where he had several small replicas made. Seeing one of these replicas in an art store in the vicinity of East 52nd Street and Fifth Avenue, Mr. Lambert was so impressed with its beauty that he purchased the rare clock for his castle residence alongside of Garret Mountain. Here he placed it in a position of honor in his main gallery."

CORTELYOU, J. W., *Morris Town*. The author hopefully thought that here was another maker of shelf clocks in New Jersey (the other was Aaron Dodd Crane). Research divulged, however, that Cortelyou was a merchant. The owner of the clock, Dr. Robert Burns of Palisade described the movement as of the "Salem Bridge" type.

CORTELYOU & WYCOFF, *New Brunswick*. The following advertisement appeared in the *Guardian*, or New Brunswick *Advertiser* over the date, December 31, 1807.

    Albany Street, New Brunswick
    Four doors below the Post Office
    Cortelyou & Wycoff
    Clock and Watch Makers

Shelf clock carrying the name of J. W.
Cortelyou and owned by Dr. Robert
Burns of Palisade.

There appeared in the advertisement the usual petition for the public's "favours" then the mention of items for sale, "spoons, bracelets, finger rings, ear hoops, lockets, hooks and eyes, netting (knitting??) needles, thimbles, pen knives, sleeve buttons, sugar tongs," etc., etc. The advertisement ended, "also musical and eight-day clocks." Another advertisement was used in the same paper in 1808 to notify removal of the business to Burnet Street.

CORY, A. M., *New Providence.* Patent No. 301,215, July 1884 for a Universal Clock.

CRAIG, SAMUEL, *Spotswood Area, Monmouth County.* Before 1746. In the *New Jersey Archives* it was found that the inventory of Craig's estate included 492.17.3 in money, a Negro boy, silver tankard, and instruments and material for making clocks and watches.

CRANE, AARON DODD, *Caldwell, Belleville,* and *Newark, New Jersey,* and *Boston, Massachusetts.* Born 1804, died 1860. Crane was born in Caldwell, New Jersey, on May 8, 1804 (his life paralleled that of Abraham Lincoln, separated in age by just five years). The Crane family was of high caliber including farmers, doctors, teachers, founders of cities (Montclair, New Jersey was once called Cranetown), merchants, inventors, and holders of public office. Crane's lineage went back through Bethuel, Jonas, William, Major Nathaniel, Azakiah to Jasper Crane, who arrived in New England from England in 1639, then moved to New Jersey, and in 1666 was one of the founders of the city of Newark. We have found nothing of Crane's schooling or how he learned clockmaking. He was born on a farm in what is now West Caldwell. The farm was then owned by his grandfather Jonas, father Bethuel not inheriting the "Homestead" until 1806. Crane was the oldest of seven children and was reared in what was probably humble though comfortable surroundings. At the age of 25, while still living in Caldwell, Crane obtained his first patent on March 18, 1829. We cannot assume that the 1829 patent was for a yearclock or even that it was for a Torsion Pendulum Clock. These characteristics were specific qualifications of his later Patent, No. 1973, obtained in Newark, New Jersey, February 10, 1841. Since Crane's patent, No. 12,196, for a torsion pendulum having "two or more weights or balls" is dated January 9, 1855, we may rightly assume that all of Crane's clocks manufactured with this type pendulum, postdate the single ball type by at least fourteen years. The multiple-balled torsion pendulum was claimed by Crane to be temperature compensating "making all its vibrations isochronal."

Aaron Dodd Crane and his Astronomical Clock. This photograph
was made in Newton, Massachusetts about 1850. Only four of
these clocks are known, three complete clocks and one clock in
parts. The clock shown here is now in the Smithsonian Institution in Washington, D. C.

January 12, 1831, was the next date we found important in the life of Crane. On this day he married Sarah A. Campbell in the First Presbyterian Church in Caldwell, New Jersey. From this marriage were born five children, Abby-Maria, Moses Griffin (about whom more later), Augustus Smith, Mathew Henderson, and Louisa. In 1839–41 Crane lived at Halsey Street near Broad Street in Newark, New Jersey. It was while here that he obtained his Patent No. 1973, before mentioned. A fine example of this single-ball type movement, in an Empire style case, is owned by H. B. Burk of Nutley, New Jersey.

Crane was listed in the directories as "Clockmaker, Belleville, New Jersey" during 1842–43 and in 1843–48 he is listed as of Belleville

---

Specification of a patent for an improvement in the plan of Construct-
    ing Clocks. Granted to AARON D. CRANE, *Caldwell, Essex coun-*
    ty, New Jersey, March 18, 1829.

BE it known that I, the said Aaron D. Crane, have invented a new and useful improvement in the making of clocks, which invention is as follows. This improvement, in the time part of the clock, consists in making it with only two wheels. One wheel with a barrel, similar to that of a common clock, only much smaller; this wheel drives a second wheel, which has pointed teeth, like those of the swing wheel of a common clock. The teeth of this wheel work on a small pallet, projecting from an arbor, on the back end of which is fixed a rack with twenty-nine teeth. The wheel acting on the pallet of this arbor, throws the rack back, when the wheel is locked, and the rack is carried forward by a light weight attached to it, and the teeth of the rack, acting on a pallet on the arbor, to which the stirrup, or guide, is fixed, keeps the pendulum in motion.

The pendulum rod is about six inches and a half long, with a very light bob, and has a balance attached to it, consisting of a slender bar about ten inches long, with a weight of six ounces at each end.

The striking part has only one wheel, which has pointed teeth, which works on a pallet in the hammer arbor, and causes it to strike the hour; and the time between the strokes is regulated by a balance attached to an arbor running through the clock, with a pallet working in the teeth of the striking wheel.

The hour is struck on strings of wire, or cat-gut, drawn over a box of thin boards about two feet long, and three inches wide.

The hands are carried without wheels. A pipe, or socket, slips into the arbor of the centre wheel, to which the minute hand is fixed, and on the back end of the pipe is fixed a spiral piece of brass, which, as it revolves, raises a hook which catches a notch in a plate on the back end of the hour socket, and moves the hour hand. All these several parts of a clock, I claim as my own invention.

                                                    AARON D. CRANE.

Copy of Crane's first patent. Provided by Fred
Selchow from the collection at Franklin Institute
in Philadelphia.

The Crane escapement, the hallmark of his clocks. Working with the escape wheel are two pawls or detents. These work alternately and as each one leaves the wheel, it receives the motion which it transfers to the torsion pendulum, keeping it in oscillation.

still, but now for the first time as "One Year Clockmaker." We quote from the *History of Essex and Hudson Counties, New Jersey,* as follows:

"In 1845, A. D. Crane being the inventor of a year clock carried on its manufacture in a small way. The firm was James R. Mills and Co. Soon after a more extensive company was formed known as the Year Clock Company. The stockholders were James R. Mills, Josiah Rhodes, Henry K. Cadmus, Abraham V. Speers, and others. They leased the mill occupied by Josiah Rhodes (formerly used by him in the processing of furs) and engaged quite extensively in manufacturing these clocks, and lost several thousand dollars in the business. They continued the business about two years when, after the failure of the business Josiah Rhodes started a grist mill and kept a flour and feed store there for some years. The mill burned down in 1858."

In this venture, as in all others that were to follow, Crane, it seems, remained the inventor, the mechanic, the maker of things. He did not here or ever anywhere team up with an entrepeneur who could help him to "reap the harvest"; to gain the prestige we too often give only to men who accumulate money. James R. Mills did make some effort at creating a market for Crane's clocks. He opened an office in New York City and did some advertising. Daggett's *New York City Directory* for 1845–46 lists "Mills, J. R. & Co., Clock Manufacturers, 109 Fulton Street, h. New Jersey (109 Fulton bet. William & Dutch)."

From 1845–57 the Newark, New Jersey directories have Crane back in Newark again. This time at 6 Lombardy Street. There is no listing of him in 1857–58, but in the directory of 1858–59 and of 1859–60 he is listed as "One Year Clockmaker, Boston, Mass." The persistent impecuniousness that dogged Crane was pathetically evidenced by an entry in the Newark Tax Collectors Book in 1852. It mentions "Aaron D. Crane at 6 Lombardy Street (Lamp and Watch District). Personal property $200.00, Total City Tax, $1.86." Alongside this entry the Tax Book notes non-payment of the personal assessment. No real estate assessment appears. Lest the reader be misled, as indeed the writer was at first, the "Lamp and Watch District" mentioned above did *not* mean that lamps and watches were manufactured in this area, but that this district had become sufficiently populated as to be entitled to street lamps and the surveillance of a watchman.

Crane's exodus to Boston and its environs seems to have been a gravitation toward the mecca of clockmakers of the time. He thought, perhaps, that here surely he would be appreciated and win the recognition so far denied him. He was joined in Boston in 1858 by his son Moses Griffin. They joined with others to form the "Turret and Marine Clock Company." Note that on the business card of that company the name of Aaron Crane is conspicuous by its absence,

TURRET AND MARINE CLOCK CO.
5 & 13 Water Street, Boston, Mass.,

Manufacture, and are prepared to furnish at short notice,

Crane's Patent Escapement Tower Clock,

The Patent Universal Clock, indicating the time on any number of dials, throughout a building.

THE PATENT ESCAPEMENT FIRE ALARM.
—ALSO—
House, Office, Calender, Marine and Watch Clocks, and Regulators.

Also—Agents for the sale of Church and other kinds of

BELLS.

COLLINS STEVENS,   GEO. F. WALKER, Agt.   MOSES G. CRANE.

Business card of the Turret and Marine Clock Co. The clocks of this company were made under the patents of Aaron Dodd Crane. The Moses G. Crane in the card was Aaron Dodd's son.

A rare Crane single-ball torsion pendulum month clock. This one has but seven wheels in the entire movement which has both time and strike. Its extreme simplicity is another indication of Crane's genius. The "walking type" of escapement, the clover leaf motion, and the single-ball torsion pendulum make it one of the most unique of all American clocks. Owned by Dr. Alfred G. Cossidente of Brooklyn, New York.

Rear view of the movement of the Crane single-ball torsion pendulum clock shown in the previous photograph.

Front view of the movement of the Crane single-ball clock.

CRANE'S
Patent Month Clocks,
MANUFACTURED BY

J. R. MILLS & CO.
BELLEVILLE, NEW JERSEY.

Warranted Superior Time Keepers.

Directions to set this Clock Running:

Stand the Clock in a perpendicular position; take out the back, put on the weights, taking care that the cords are on the pullies; then wind it up turning to the right, put the ball on the hook at the lower end of the Pendulum Spring, and give it two revolutions.

To set the Time:

The minute hand may be turned any number of hours forward; but not backward when within fifteen minutes of striking, nor further back than the figure XII.

To set the Striking:

Gently pull a Wire on the left of the Pendulum Spring, until it strikes the right hour.

To regulate the Clock:

This is done by means of a small screw on the side of the Pendulum Ball. If the Clock goes too slow, turn it to the right; if too fast, turn it to the left.

N. B. When the Clock is removed, take off the Pendulum Ball and weights; to get at the weights, take out the back.

Description of the Improvement in this Clock:

The great Improvement in the Time Part consists principally in the Escapement, which may be called a Frictionless Escapement; and in the Regulating Motion, which may be called a Rotary or Torsion Pendulum. The Ball is hollow, and suspended by a steel spring; near the upper end of the spring is an arm in the form of a Crank; the revolving of the ball twists the spring, and causes the arm to perform an arch, acting upon and receiving the impulse from the Swing Wheel, by means of a lever connected with the arm and the Pallets or Escapement; which impulse is carried through the spring to the ball, and keeps it in motion. The spring in a quiescent state is longest; by its being twisted either way from that state is shortened and the ball made to rise, returning by the re-action of the spring, and the force of gravity receiving the impulse from the maintaining power at each return. Any difference of friction or maintaining power in this Clock, will not effect the time given by this Pendulum, its revolutions or vibrations are rendered perfectly isochronal, by the influence that the torsion of the spring has in its re-action upon the force of gravity of the ball. The different degrees of temperature do not effect the time given by this pendulum. The time it would lose by the expansion of the spring in length, is acurately counteracted by the time it gains by its expansion in width and thickness; and the time it would lose by the expansion of the ball outward from its axis of motion, is accurately counteracted and compensated for by an adjustment inside the ball. The improvement in the striking part consists principally in the application of a Rotary Hammer.

The advantages of this Clock, are

1st. That very little care is required in setting it up, in consequence of its not being so liable to be put out of beat, as other clocks.

2nd. It requires no Oil on the Pallets or teeth of the Swing Wheel, there being no friction between them, and the number of the revolutions of the Swing Wheel are sixty times less, or in other words in sixty years in making as many revolutions as the thirty-nine inch, or second Pendulum Clock does in one year. And it requires more than thirty times less maintaining power; consequently a very large amount less of friction and wear, than in other Clocks: and therefore the motion much more regular.

3rd. It will run thirty-three days with one winding up; is silent, other than striking the hour; is simple, easily adjusted and regulated; and when so, the time will not be altered, as in other Clocks, by the difference of temperature, the density of the air, or by an increase of friction; as it performs its movements always in the same or equal time.

Label in the case of the Crane single-ball clock.

Another Crane single-ball torsion pendulum month clock. Owned by Fred Selchow of Concord, New Hampshire.

making evident the typical introversion of the inventor and the mechanic, leaving to others, to his own detriment perhaps, the putting up of a front.

It was at this time that Crane obtained another patent, No. 19,351, dated February 16, 1858. This was for a church clock, so called by Crane although the U. S. Patent Office labeled it a "Public Clock." Miss Elizabeth King Crane, a granddaughter, described to the writer what might have been this clock. She remembered seeing in the home of her father (Augustus Smith) a clock that her grandfather had made. It was, she said, about 16 inches in diameter, round in shape, with a wide ornamental border. On the dial, between the numeral VI and the hole accommodating the hour wheel post, was a glass covered aperture through which could be seen the moving torsion pendulum. The whereabouts of this clock is not known to any one to whom the writer has mentioned it.

Aaron Dodd Crane was of course an inventor, and a maker of clocks. His son Moses Griffin Crane was, as a young man, a repairer of watches and clocks, and later he was a machinist and inventor. Evidence points that he probably manufactured some clocks. Regarding his inventions, we quote from a letter sent us by the Gamewell Company of Newton Upper Falls, Massachusetts. "Every manufacturer of fire alarm boxes in the world today probably employs his principle." Despite the notoriety and wealth that his other activities won him, Moses Griffin Crane spent almost all of his life actively engaged in some endeavor that involved clocks. In Brooks Palmer's *Book of American Clocks* he lists, "Converse & Crane: Boston. Ca. 1870." That Crane was Moses Griffin Crane who with Alfred C. Converse was active in making tower clocks. They operated at 130 Washington Street in Boston, Massachusetts from 1864 to 1869. One of Moses Griffin's many inventions was No. 33,462 dated October 8, 1861, and entitled "Improvement in Tower Clocks."

Another son of Aaron Dodd Crane, Augustus Smith Crane of Newark was an inventor too. Four of his patents were concerned with electric clocks. Newton Crane, a grandson of Aaron D. had 28 patents issued to him. It was recorded by himself that he had "made" over 70 inventions.

There are those who have said that Aaron Dodd Crane was a genius. This we have no desire to refute nor the ability to affirm. We have read and heard of and from men of great understanding of clocks, who have examined Crane's clocks and said, "Ingenious!"

In the design of his clocks, Crane appreciated and reached to a high degree the features desirable in all mechanical things: (A) The use of a minimum of power (the weights in his clocks are measured in

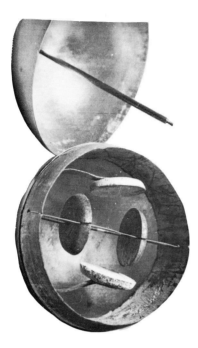

Detail of the pendulum ball. Turning the slotted screw head on the outside of the hollow ball in one direction moves the two weights closer together to make the clock run faster. Turning the screw in the opposite direction separates the weights to make the clock run slower.

Front view of the movement of the Crane single-ball clock.

Crane six-ball year clock. Collection of
the Newark Museum.

Crane single-ball year clock (top left) owned by Alfred Butler of Hope. Top right, interior of the pendulum ball showing construction. Regulating is done by turning the screw. Bottom, front view of the movement.

Silver medal awarded to Crane by the American Institute of New York in 1855 for his invention of a "Lathe for turning irregular forms." Although the name Tomkins appears on the medal, it is not mentioned in the patent, even as a witness. Daniel F. and John T. Tomkins were listed as two of the incorporators of the Crane Lathe Company. It might reasonably be assumed that Crane made some sort of concession to the Tomkinses, and so both names appeared on the medal.

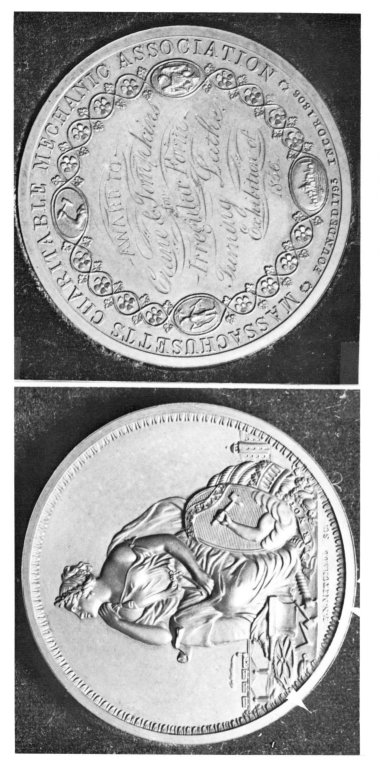

Bronze medal awarded to Crane and Tomkins for "Irregular Form Turning Lathe," by the Massachusetts Charitable Mechanic Association in 1856.

Crane three-ball eight-day clock. Although this and other Crane clocks were
sold from a New York City address, all of
Crane's clocks were manufactured in
New Jersey.

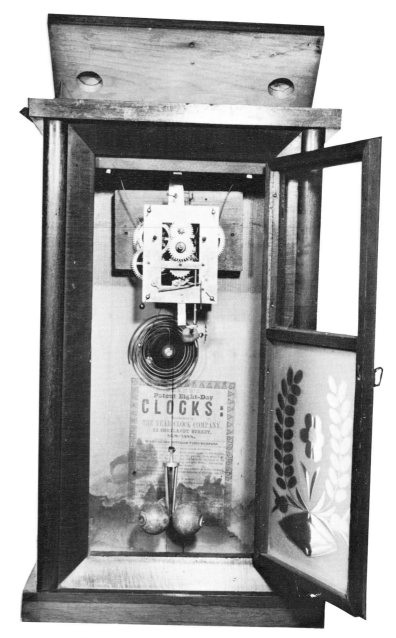

"Inside story." This movement is identical to the one that Crane skeletonized for exhibition purposes.

Crane Astronomical Clock whose label states it was manufactured in Newark, New Jersey. Owned by Smithsonian Institution in Washington.

Crane Astronomical Clock bearing the label of Boston Clock Company. Owned by Col. Turner W. Gilman (U.S.A. Ret.) of Hanover, Massachusetts. Photograph by the owner.

Side view of the movement of the Crane
Astronomical Clock shown in the previous photograph.

Rear view of the Crane Astronomical Clock.

The third of the three known Crane Astronomical Clocks.

ounces rather than pounds) (B) and a minimum of friction (his design of escapement in his torsion pendulum invention is relatively frictionless). A show of appreciation of Crane's originality is found in the brochure of the once excellent clock collection at the Mitchell Inn in Middletown, New York. In describing the Crane clock (No. 280 in the brochure) it is said, "This early American clock employs one of of the most unusual set of works of any clock in the collection." The comparative rarity and the striking difference (pun intended) has made the Crane clock a prized piece in any collection.

In the writer's opinion some of Crane's clocks have an aesthetic appeal and a European sophistication much apart from the almost primitive simplicity of most American clocks of the time. .(An exception is the Oliver B. Marsh clock.) This is particularly true of a clock bearing Crane's name on a brass plate above the dial. Although not large, it has a quality of solidity approaching the massive. Without being garish it is richly ornamental and overall it is an extremely handsome piece.

Mrs. Carrie Crane Ingalls, another granddaughter of Aaron D., wrote to the author that in her knowledge four clocks of this type were made. We know of all four. One at the Smithsonian Institution in Washington, D. C. is the "Newark" clock. This particular type of clock also indicates astronomical phenomena. The other similar clock we found in Boston. The two clocks are almost identical, with the most obvious difference being the identifying plates. The one in Washington gives Newark, New Jersey as the maker's address, and the one in Boston has engraved on it "Boston Clock Co. A. D. Crane Pat., 375 days, Patented Feb. 10, 1841, Extended Dec. 15, 1854, Improved June 22nd, 1852 and Jan. 9th 1855." The third clock is owned by Col. Turner W. Gilman. The fourth, in parts, is owned by Dr. A. Cossidante of Brooklyn, New York.

Another fine example of Crane's work is his "skeleton" clock. This is one, and as far as we know the only one, that Crane skeletonized. This was done at an obvious attempt at ostentation for this clock was then offered to the American Institute for exhibition at their fair in New York City in October 1842. The Judges Report reads in part, "We give it as our opinion that No. 365 is the best of clocks. Made by Aaron D. Crane the inventor (a skeleton)." The award was a Silver Medal. (A Silver Medal was also awarded Crane and Tompkins by the American Institute in 1855 for his invention of a "Spoke Lathe." His Pat. No. 11,518. A Bronze Medal, for this same invention was awarded by the Massachusetts Charitable Mechanic Association in 1856).

Whether it was an effort to procure a salable clock or whether he was following a creative compulsion, Crane made a great variety of clocks. Those who are interested in the technical aspects of clocks will find delight in the many ingenious mechanical concepts employed by him.

There are the Single Ball and the Multiple Ball types, Eight Day, Thirty Day, and of course Year Clocks (376 day). Crane worked on Shelf Clocks, Wall Clocks, and Tower Clocks. The cases of his Shelf Clocks were mostly in "Empire" style. This case has its border receding from the edge in a straight line rather than the shallow double curve of the conventional OG. One type of Crane clock was described to us as being "In a 'French type' glass case, the weight concealed by a false back." We cannot confirm that such a "Crane" clock exists.

Regarding Crane's activities with tower clocks, we were told by two of his granddaughters, Miss Elizabeth King Crane and Mrs. Anna Crane Beers (separately and independent of each other) that "Grandfather Crane had something to do with a Tower Clock in the First Presbyterian Church in Orange, New Jersey." This church was then on the corner of Main and Day Streets and we have found references in the history of the Church that a clock *was* installed in 1855 (when Aaron Dodd was listed in Newark, a short distance away). Unfortunately in April 1927 the church burned, destroying the clock and all records of it.

In 1860, in a final bid to market his wares, Crane formed "The Crane Lathe Company" based on his Patent No. 11,518. This company was incorporated in Newark, New Jersey (it would seem that Crane must have done a great deal of commuting between Newark and Boston). The authorized capital stock was 1,000 shares of $100.00 each, par value. The incorporators were Aaron D. Crane, Daniel F. Tompkins, Lebbeus B. Miller, James H. Hill, Daniel Holsman, L. Spencer Goble, Henry E. Richards and John T. Tompkins. Three of these incorporators we "looked up" and found were men of the highest integrity and reputation, interested in sound investment, not risky speculation. Mr. Lebbeus B. Miller, in particular, was himself a machinist, superintendent of The Manhattan Firearms Factory and later supervisor, then general superintendent of the Singer Sewing Machine Company. The confidence of such men was certainly an attestation of Crane's mechanical ability and soundness of thought. Other inventions by Crane, bequeathing the rights to these in his will, were for water meters and calendars. It is mentioned in his will also that, "I give and bequeath to my son Moses G. Crane the several patent rights issued to me by the Patent Office of the United States for inventions made by me and now held by me under agreements with and licenses from me by the Turret & Marine Clock Company in

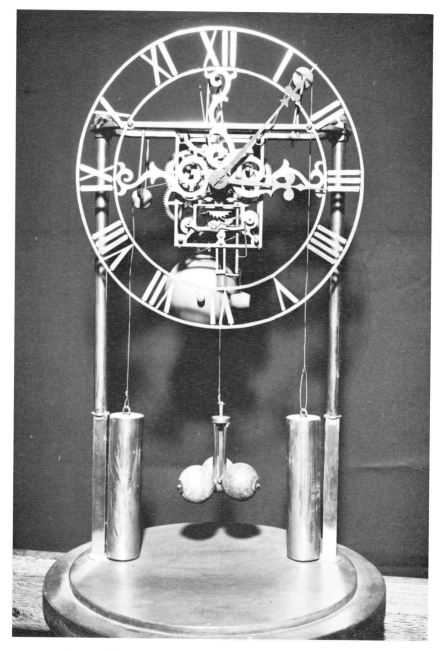

Only known "skeletonized" Crane clock. Made for exhibition at the Fifteenth Annual Fair of the American Institute in New York City in October 1842. The dial was sawed and filed out of a single sheet of brass. The judges declared it to be "The best specimen of clocks." Owned by the author.

The judges' report on the Crane skeletonized clock. Courtesy of the New York Historical Society.

One of Crane's few four-ball month
clocks. Owned by Robert Brown of
Millington.

The Crane month clock with the door
open to show the four-ball torsion pendulum.

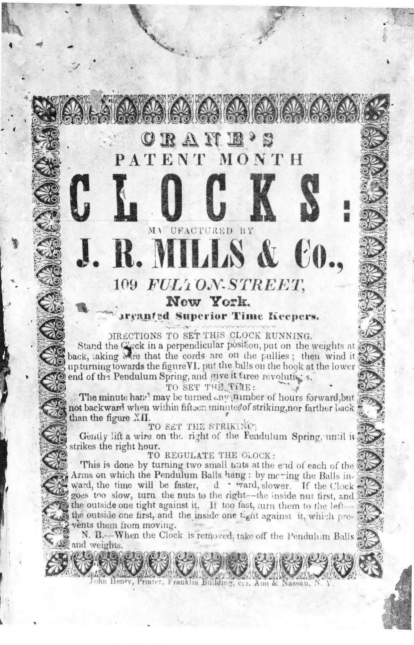

CRANE'S
PATENT MONTH
CLOCKS:
MANUFACTURED BY
J. R. MILLS & Co.,
109 FULTON-STREET,
New York.
Warranted Superior Time Keepers.

DIRECTIONS TO SET THIS CLOCK RUNNING.
Stand the Clock in a perpendicular position, put on the weights at back, taking care that the cords are on the pullies ; then wind it up turning towards the figure VI. put the balls on the hook at the lower end of the Pendulum Spring, and give it three revolutions.

TO SET THE TIME:
The minute hand may be turned any number of hours forward, but not backward when within fifteen minutes of striking, nor farther back than the figure XII.

TO SET THE STRIKING:
Gently lift a wire on the right of the Pendulum Spring, until it strikes the right hour.

TO REGULATE THE CLOCK:
This is done by turning two small nuts at the end of each of the Arms on which the Pendulum Balls hang : by moving the Balls inward, the time will be faster, downward, slower. If the Clock goes too slow, turn the nuts to the right—the inside nut first, and the outside one tight against it. If too fast, turn them to the left— the outside one first, and the inside one tight against it, which prevents them from moving.

N. B.—When the Clock is removed, take off the Pendulum Balls and weights.

John Henry, Printer, Franklin Building, ccr. Ann & Nassau, N. Y.

Label of the Crane month clock.

Boston." (Proof of Aaron Dodd Crane's Tower Clock activities.) Also, Crane mentioned in his Will, "I desire my Executors to procure such Patents for my unpatented inventions." How many or what else his fertile mind devised of other things we have not discovered.

About Aaron Dodd Crane the man, Mrs. Carrie Crane Ingalls says, "He was a quiet, silent man, absorbed in his inventions. He had a very high forehead and dignified manner and fine features. His last years were passed with my father (Moses Griffin Crane) where he was ill. My mother often told me how he sat at the window with a shawl around his shoulders, always gentle and uncomplaining."

Lest the writer seem too biased or prejudiced about Crane, we submit another opinion. About Aaron Dodd Crane, H. Alan Lloyd wrote in his book *Old Clocks*, published in 1958 "Whilst in the early years of American clockmaking ideas and designs were copied largely from England, the finishing note of this chapter (titled "American Clocks") will be an example where the American horologist led the world." Mr. Lloyd then goes on about Crane's torsion pendulum clocks particularly the astronomical clock.

On March 10, 1860, Aaron Dodd Crane died of "consumption," on Cottage Street in the Roxbury Section of Boston, age 55 years and 10 months. He lies buried in the Forest Hills Cemetery in that city, in a grave that was owned by his son Moses Griffin Crane. There is no stone to mark his grave.

CRANE, AUGUSTUS SMITH, *Newark*. Son of Aaron Dodd Crane. Born in Newark December 31, 1834. Married Henrietta Palmer on May 1, 1862. Employed at Durand and Company, Jewelers and while there invented a device to weave gold wire. His several patents on electric clocks were:
> 1833, No. 286,181, Secondary Electric Clock
> 1883, No. 286,623, Actuating Device for a Secondary Clock
> 1884, No. 301,569, Electromagnetic Clock
> 1885, No. 311,234, Electric Clock

CRANE, JONAS SMITH, *Newark*. Listed in the city directory 1843–44. In the same directory he advertised, "Clock and watch maker, 262 Broad Street (Adjoining the Old Bank). Keeps constantly on hand a good Assortment of Jewelry. Particular attention paid to Repairing."

CROW, WILLIAM, *Salem*. Birth date about 1715. Died 1758. In the New Jersey Archives; Abstract of Wills is recorded, "1734, December 4, Songhurst, Editha of Salem Town & County, will of: Proceeds of estate to be divided among my children Mary Crow, George Crow,

Clock by William Crow of Salem. Owned by Salem County Historical Society.

Dial of the William Crow clock shown in the previous photograph.

and William Crow. Friend (this probably in the Quaker usage) Benj. Acton to assist daughter Mary (the executrix) in the management until my two sons will be 21." Proved Feb. 10, 1735.

The George Crow, mentioned in the above paragraph as brother of William, is mentioned in Palmer's *The Book of American Clocks* as a clockmaker of Wilmington, Delaware. Further proof of their relationship is given, again in the Abstract of Wills, "Crow, William, 1758, of Salem Town and County Inst. Susanah, Widow resigns her right to administer on his estate to Brother George Crow and Samuel Tyler, 1758 June 20. Bond of George Crow, Wilmington, New Castle County upon Delaware and Samuel Tyler of Salem, tanner, as administrators."

CUNNINGHAM, JOSEPH, *Trenton*. Died 1869.

DAVENPORT, ISIAH, *Raccoon, Woolwich Township, Gloucester County*. Before 1773. His will, dated October 22, 1773 and proved January 8, 1774, identifies Davenport as "Clockmaker." Further identification of Isiah Davenport is the will of Isaac Davenport of Greenwich, Gloucester County, May 28, 1766, wherein, "Isiah Davenport, Clockmaker" is the administrator. The Davenports were, firstly, from Whittington in Derby County, England. A Francis Davenport lived next to John Hollinshead in South Jersey in 1673.

DAVIS, JAMES, *Bloomfield*. At work 1812. Advertised in the *Centinel* (sic) *of Freedom* in the January 7, 1817 issue; "The Subscriber takes this method to acknowledge his obligations to his friends and customers for past favors and solicits their attention as he again commenced the Silversmithing, Watch and Clock Making at his old stand near the Academy, where he will devote his most steady attention. All persons favouring him with their custom will be faithfully attended to and honestly dealt with. Bloomfield Dec. 28, 1816. James Davis"

Of Davis' clocks, one is known about. Oscar Appel, a dealer in Paterson, related that he had owned and then sold a James Davis clock. Mr. Appel had a small color photo of the clock and had made some detailed notes about it. In his notes was recorded that the case was of mahogany, 8 feet 3 inches tall. The clock had a painted iron dial with calendar and moon phase. In the painting of the moon phase part of the dial was a ship with an American flag. Two oddities were noted by Mr. Appel. The bell on the clock was inscribed, "S. B. Dod" (this could have been Stephen Baldwin Dod noted elsewhere herein), and the dial was inscribed "Curtis" on the back. The Pendulum bob was unusual in that it was inscribed; "1812, James Davis, Bloomfield, Warranted, No. 5."

DAWES, WILLIAM P., *Elizabeth Town*. Born 1746. Died August 28, 1811. Married Sarah Miller, granddaughter of Aaron Miller. Was the "Dawes" of the Dawes and Woodruff who advertised in the *Jersey Journal*, "GOLD AND SILVERSMITHS. The subscribers take this method of informing the Public that they have entered into the line of their profession under the firm of Dawes and Woodruff in Elizabeth Town at the shop formerly occupied by Robinson Thomas as a store, where they carry on the different branches of CLOCK AND WATCH-MAKING and SILVER PLATING..." Elizabeth Town June 23, 1804.

DECKER, J. *Sparta*. Patent No. 163,531, 1867. Alarm Clock.

DICKENSON, T. L., *Dover*. Listed in *Kirkbride's Directory* 1850–51.

DOD (also spelled Dodd), ABNER, *Newark*. Born, March 20, 1772. Died, September 29, 1847. Second son of Lebbeus, advertised in the *Sentinel of Freedom*.

Abner Dod

CLOCK Maker, Mathematical Instrument Maker,
Gun Smith, Iron Turner, &c., &c., One door East
of the Union School House, in New Street.
Newark May 3, 1825

Listed in the *Newark Directory* 1835–36 as "Clockmaker and Gunsmith, h. 35 Washington and New."

DOD, DANIEL, *Mendham* and *Elizabeth Town*. Born September 8, 1778. Died May 9, 1823. It is noted in the Dod & Burnet "*Genealogy of the Male Descendants of Daniel Dod of Branford Conn. 1646–1863,*" that Daniel Dod was born in the Northern part of Virginia. His parents were however natives of Newark. The family returned to New Jersey during his early youth and settled in Mendham. "Daniel was bred by his father to the business of clock and watchmaker, mathematical instrument maker and land surveyer...son of Lebbeus (he) was a man of rare mathematical and mechanical genius." Two clocks are known of Daniel Dod's make. One in Mendham and one in California. No particularly outstanding qualities were found in the clock examined.

Evidence to attest the diversity of Daniel Dod's talents is found in the detailed account of the First Presbyterian Church in Horseneck-Caldwell, New Jersey. This in the book *A Puritan Heritage* by Lynn G. Lockward. Mr. Lockward wrote, "It was in this year of 1811 that the Society purchased a bell for the Meeting House. The bell cost eighty dollars and weighed two hundred and eighty-nine pounds. It was cast and owned by Daniel Dod of Mendham, and had been cast for the Newark Court House, but proved to be too small."

Daniel Dod was best known for his inventions and making of the machinery for developing steam power. It was his machinery and boilers that powered the first steamboat that crossed the Atlantic Ocean, the steamship *Savannah*. The *Savannah* crossed from Savannah, Georgia to Liverpool, England in twenty-five days. Dod was killed on board the steamship *Patent* when a boiler burst.

DOD, LEBBEUS, *Mendham*. Born in Newark February 15, 1739. Died in Mendham March 31, 1816. Dod was brought to Mendham from Newark as a child about 1745. He was variously a farmer, mathematical instrument maker, clockmaker, Revolutionary soldier (attaining the rank of Captain in the artillery), and armorer for the Continental cause. His musket armory was next to his house, still standing in 1940, at Mendham. Lebbeus Dod was in several ways very close to the war of the Revolution. Aside from his service to the cause he, it is recorded in the old record books of Mendham, collected for taking up "strays" in 1765, 1767, and 1770.

He deposed, on December 20, 1784, as "Captain Lebbeus Dod," that he witnessed the marriage of his sister Deborah to William Minthorn, who lost his life at the Battle of Yorktown, in 1781. (*Proceedings of the New Jersey Historical Society*, Vol. 1, 1916, p. 156.) Lebbeus Dod married Mary Baldwin, daughter of Caleb and Hannah (Ricky) on January 5, 1764. Of the seven children, four

Clock by Daniel Dod, owned by Mr. and
Mrs. Zachariah Belcher of Mendham

Clock by Lebbeus Dod. The cabinet is of mahogany and while there is not the often-found evidence of a highly skilled cabinetmaker, such as inlay work and turning or carving, the style and proportions are quite pleasing. Owned by Mr. and Mrs. Willard Randolph van Liew of Montclair.

Dial of the Lebbeus Dod clock. It is hand hammered and the spandrels are of brass.

Boss of the dial on the Lebbeus Dod clock showing the unusual inscription.

Movement of the Lebbeus Dod clock. The similarity between this movement and those of Aaron Miller and Isaac Brokaw gives cause to believe that it might have been bought from either. The wood winding drums, the position of the count wheel, the "streak of lightning" lifting level (difficult to see in this photograph), and even the style of the dial all bear a strong resemblence to the clocks of Miller and Brokaw. Variances found are the manner in which the calendar wheel, in back of the dial, is attached, and in the manner in which the back plate is cut out, almost as though the maker was going to "skeletonize" the movement. The boss is also attached to the dial in a unique manner—with a rivet.

daughters and three sons, two sons, Abner and Daniel are herein noted as clockmakers also.

The clock illustrated in the photograph is exceptional in that on the boss of the dial is inscribed, not only that it was "Made by Lebbeus Dod," but also inscribed, "For Doctor Ebenezer Blatchley, Mendham." Why this was done can only be conjectured. Doctor Blatchley (as Dod spelled his name) was almost the same age as Lebbeus, being born in 1735 and having died in 1805. Since the two were boys together in the same small town and growing up together in the same town, perhaps they were such friends that the clock was made as a gift of friendship. Or perhaps, being the sire of seven children, the clock was a token of appreciation for services rendered by the doctor. For whatever reason Dod may have put the name there with his, it adds greatly to the historic significance to the clock for Doctor Blatchley went on to become one of the founders of the New Jersey Medical Society and became the progenitor of several doctors.

DOD, STEPHEN, *Newark*. Born March 1, 1770 in Mendham. Died March 28, 1855. He is buried in Mount Pleasant Cemetery, Newark. "Like his father (Lebbeus), he was mechanically inclined and learned from him at Mendham the crafts of instrument maker, silversmith, and watchmaker. Moved to Newark in 1817 where he was in the business of surveying and real estate. He was Justice of the Peace, city surveyor, and Mayor in 1844. He lived at 276 Broad Street between Bank and Market Streets. His maps of Newark, drawn from his own surveys, appear in all Newark city directories from 1847 to 1863. He was New Jersey Assemblyman from Morris County from 1807 to 1812. He married Mehetabel Gould of Caldwell on June 4, 1796. They had four children, Mary, Lebbeus, John, and Sarah Anne. He was also Assemblyman from Essex County, and he was the Speaker-Pro-Tem of the Assembly during the session of 1837."— From *Genealogy of the Daniel Dod Family in America, 1646 to 1940.*

EGERTON, MATTHEW, SR., *New Brunswick*, 1740–1802. Was one of the very fine cabinetmakers of New Jersey. His shop as indicated by his labels was on Burnet Street. There is little doubt that he trained his son Matthew Egerton, Jr. in the same craft, their work is so similar that, if not identifiable by a label, it is almost impossible to distinguish one from the other. Either or both made cases for the clocks of the Brokaws (see photo), for Leslie and Williams, and probably for others. Several clocks, not identified by any name on the dial, were found to have the Egerton quality about them.

Script label of Matthew Egerton, Sr. on the case of an Isaac
Brokaw clock. The label is paper measuring $3\frac{3}{8}$ by $1\frac{1}{4}$ inches. The
script is hand written with ink.

EGERTON, MATTHEW, JR., *New Brunswick*, 1785–1837. His labels found in the clocks of Brokaw, Lupp, and Leslie and Williams read "Joiner and Cabinetmaker."

ELY, HUGH, *Trenton*. 1803–1820. Born November 5, 1783. Married to Hannah Wilson. Died in Trenton January 6, 1829. Son of John and Margaret (Richards) Ely of Solebury, Pa. Had shop in New Hope, Pa. in 1800. In the history of the Ely-Revell-Stacye families by Reuben P., Warren S. and Daniel B. Ely it is stated, "He was considered an expert in the manufacture of tall grandfather clocks. He made at least one musical tall clock that played the tunes Nancy Dawson, Yankee Doodle, and Beggar Girl."

EMMONS, ERASTUS, *Trenton*, 1800–1820. From the character of his advertisement Emmons was a repairer although possibly a maker of clocks. No clock is known to the writer. His advertisement in the *Federalist* on July 16, 1807 read in part, "All orders in the line of clock repairing will be thankfully received and punctually executed." His shop was near that of William Leslie and opposite the Indian Queen Tavern. The temperance wave throughout the country in 1807 prompted Emmons to write, in another advertisement, "... repairing and putting in due order watches, clocks, and timepieces on the shortest notice and the most reasonable terms, at his old stand in Warren Street, Trenton, nearly opposite the Temple of Bacchus, vulgarly called, the Indian Queen Tavern...."

FITCH, JOHN, *Trenton*. Was a repairer of watches and clocks. Generally credited with the invention of the steamboat.

FISCHLEIN, F., *Jersey City*. Patent No. 175,344, 1876, for Lighting Attachment for Alarm Clock.

FITZGERALD, W. H. *Carlstadt*. Patent No. 11,334, 1871, for Stem Winding Attachment.

FLEMING, J. H., *Newark*. Patent No. 411,800, 1889 for Watch Case Spring. Patent No. 420,048, 1890 for Watch Case Spring. Patent No. 440,308, 1890, for Watch Case.

FLING, DANIEL, *Mount Holly*. About 1810. Had shop on Mill Street near the Union National Bank. Left Mount Holly for Philadelphia. One clock known.

Egerton, Jr., label found in a Leslie and Williams clock. Courtesy of Monmouth County Historical Association.

FREEMAN, J. R., *Morristown*, 1850–51. Listed as clock and watchmaker in *Kirkbride's Directory*.

GAINSWORTH, WARREN. Name found cast into bell on a Morgan Hollinshead clock.

GAITHER, HENRY, *Trenton*, 1814. Partner of William J. Leslie.

GAMAGE, SAMUEL JR., *Elizabeth Town*, 1806. Shop across from Aaron Lane. Advertised in the *New Jersey Journal*, March 31 and April 8, 1806, "Samuel Gamage Jr. Clock and Watch Maker, Gold and Silver Smith and Jeweller."

GERRY, JAMES H., *Newark*. Patent No. 236,017, for Winding Attachment for Clock, 1880. This is the "attachment," applied to a clock made by the Boston Clock Company of 1884, whereby the winding of both the time and strike mainsprings is done from a single winding arbor, a forward motion of the key winding one and a reverse motion the other.

GILES, JOSEPH, *Trenton*, 1804. From Boston. Located first on Warren Street. On October 21, 1804 Giles advertised in the *Federalist* of his moving to Market Street. "Joseph Giles, clock and watchmaker, respectfully informs his customers and the public that he has moved next door to Thomas M. Potter's Medicine Store, in Market Street, where he continues the business of clockmaking and watch repairing, which he will execute on the most reasonable terms. N.B. He will warrant his work to run well for one year, the cheapest kind of watches." Although Giles differs in his terminology, in his advertisement, and refers to his "clock MAKING" and "watch REPAIRING," no clocks of his making are known to the writer. His watch paper does indicate his activities as a watch repairer.

GITHENS, WILLIAM, *Haddonfield*. About 1820. A cabinetmaker who worked with cherry, mahogany, and walnut in the Hepplewhite and Sheraton styles. Made cases for the clocks of John Whitehead. He used the serpentine broken arch in the hood with wood finials. The finials were variously ball, urn, and in one instance, a carved basket of flowers. The Sheraton influence of turned feet is evident in two of his cases. Githens shop was located on Potter Street in 1831. His son Charles followed his father's trade making, repairing and refinishing furniture. It was noted that Samuel Burroughs and Charles Githens, at this time "were the only cabinetmakers in Haddonfield and made coffins and burial cases for the dead."

GOULD, URIAH, *Mendham*, early 1800's. Of the two clocks found and examined both were of the type whereby the clockmaker used imported parts, finished and fitted them to make a clock. A characteristic found on Gould's clocks and on no other is his use of the arched or curved aperture, in the lower center of the dial, to identify himself with his work. This aperture usually reveals the days of the month, painted on a "calendar" wheel. Gould simply backed up the aperture or opening with a brass plate upon which his name is found engraved.

GRAY, RICHARDSON, *Elizabeth Town*. Born 1754. Died 1818. Cabinetmaker. Made cases for Isaac Brokaw. His place of business was bought by Burrows and Howell. In the several advertisements seen of Burrows and Howell there is no evidence that they carried on the work of cabinetmaking. All of their advertisements were for the sale of general merchandise.

Clock of Uriah Gould of Mendham.
Courtesy of Mr. and Mrs. Harold Wil-
merding of Mendham.

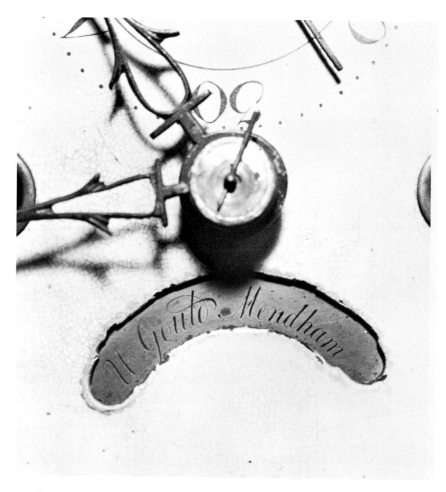

Detail of the dial of Uriah Gould's clock. Note the rather odd location of the maker's name. Both Gould clocks seen were identified
in the same manner in the same location.

Uriah Gould clock in a fine case with the center finial, apparently original, an eagle. Owned by the Municipality of Mendham.

GUILD, BENJAMIN. Probably in the Hunterdon County area during the late 1700's or early 1800's. Search in the New Jersey Archives, among wills and inventories of the Guild family has been unrewarding in the effort to find a Benjamin Guild who was mentioned as a clockmaker.

Two clocks are known, one owned by the Monmouth County Historical Association and one by William Moodie of Essex Fells. The first has only the name on the dial, the second has the name and oddly, simply "Jersey" on the dial.

GUILD, JOHN, *Pennington and Ewing area*. Born 1750, Died 1825. Married December 29, 1780 to Abigail Howell.

A clock, once owned by Karl Jacobi of Chatham and reported by him, had on the dial, the inscription, "John Guild Pennington." Another John Guild clock was reported by Mrs. Mary T. Bauer of Haddonfield and seen by her in that area. A third John Guild clock was examined and photographed by the writer, in the Vailsburg section of Newark. The movement of this clock is indistinguishable from those of Aaron Miller and/or the Brokaws (who used Miller's design). All of the Miller-Brokaw features are evident, the count wheel affixed to the great wheel on the strike side, the "streak of lightning" lifting lever, the very thin brass dial and even the upper corner of the rear plate cut off. The design and quality of the hands and dial mark this as one of the earlier clocks of New Jersey, probably before 1775.

It is noteworthy that the clock seen by the writer in Newark is owned by Mr. and Mrs. B. E. Hullfish and that Mr. Hullfish is a descendant of the Howell family. Since John Guild had married one Abigail Howell the clock has thus been a "family" clock for almost 200 years. It is serving as faithfully and well today as when it was made.

GULEBERG, C. G., *Jersey City*. Patent No. 244,451, 1881, Stem-winding Attachment for Clocks. Patent No. 260,751, 1882, Electric Clock.

GUNZ, O. F., *Rutherford*. Patents No's. 411,146 and 411,147, Stem Winding and Setting for Watch.

HACKER, MICHAEL, *New Germantown*. 1750's. Clocks marked both New Germantown and Tewksberry. Hacker was of the Moravian faith. He died in 1796.

Dial of a Benjamin Guild clock. Courtesy of the Monmouth
County Historical Association.

Clock of John Guild. The case is of mahogany and skillfully made. This photograph, taken under adverse circumstances by the author, shows one of the graceful feet and also the beaded moulding at the bottom of the base—evidences of rather sophisticated cabinet work. The cabinetmaker is unknown.

Dial of the John Guild clock of the previous photograph.

HALL, JOSIAH, *Salem*. 1803. Found in a deed dated 1804, "This indenture between Josiah Hall, of the Town of Salem, County of Salem & State of New Jersey, Clockmaker of the one part and Jacob Mulford of the same instance of the second part."

HALLIDAY, E. H., *Camden*. 1790's–1820's.

HALSEY, W. H., *Hoboken*. Patent No. 81,082, 1868, Mold for Watch Case.

HARRIS, J. C., *Bridgeton*. 1850–51. Listed in *Kirkbride's Directory*.

HART, RICHARD. Clockmaker of the Flemington area.

HAVELL, G., *Newark*. Patent No. 228,193, 1880, Clock Case.

HERON, ISAAC, *Bound Brook*. 1764. Advertised July 1764, in the *New York Mercury* of New York City, that he repaired, "All sorts of Watches, Clocks, Jewelry and Plate in Bound Brook, New Jersey."

HETZEL, JOHN M., *Newton*. 1795. Advertisement in the *Wood's Gazette* (Newark), February 18, 1795, "CLOCK MAKING. The subscriber takes this method to inform his former customers and the public in general, that he has lately set up the Clockmaking and Silversmithing business in Sussex, Township of Newton, who will make and dispatch articles in that line in the most reasonable terms, Clocks in particular. The subscriber wants immediately, two apprentices, smart active lads, about 13 or 14 years of age. John M. Hetzel." Found also in *New Jersey Wills*, "1814, May 13, Hetzel, Jacob, of Walpack Township, Sussex County dies intestate. Inventory $566.01, made by Ira Fuller, Roland Bell. Includes Clockmaker's Tools, Blacksmith's Tools. Sworn to by Michael Hetzel, Administrator, Aug. 17, 1814." The "John" and "Jacob" were probably the same man.

HEWITT, H. T., *Scotch Plains*. Patent No. 51,044, 1865, Clock Escapement.

HILL, JOAKIM, *Flemington*. Born in Amwell Township, November 25, 1783. Died in Newark, April 12, 1869 at 76 Orchard Street. Hill became a member of the Presbyterian Church in 1815 and is buried in the Presbyterian churchyard in Flemington. In a paper, read at a meeting of the Hunterdon Historical Society and subsequently published in *The Jerseyman* in 1905, Alex B. Allen wrote of an interview

Clock of Joakim Hill of Flemington.

Joakim Hill clock owned by the New Jersey Historical Society.

Part of a legal document showing the signature of Joakim Hill. Hill apparently spent much time at repair work. His signature in script is frequently found with the date of repair on the inside of the door of clock cases.

Joakim Hill clock in an especially fine
case. Courtesy of Israel Sack, Inc. of
New York.

Example of splendid New Jersey cabinetmaking—a clock case made by Oliver
Parsell of New Brunswick containing a
clock by Joakim Hill. Courtesy of Ginsburg & Levy, Inc. of New York.

Label in the case of the clock shown in the previous photograph.

he had with Miss Martha Hill, a daughter of Joakim, "She said her father was not a cabinetmaker nor did he make the dials. He purchased the cases, usually handsome solid mahogany, frequently inlaid, of a cabinetmaker near Flemington named, John Tappan." A Hill clock with an Oliver Parsell label in the case is also known Mr. Allen wrote, in his paper on Hill, a picturesque paragraph of Hill's activities as a repairman, "One of the yearly occurrences in the houses surrounding this part of the country (Flemington and environs) where an old eight-day clock ticked away the time, was the visit of Joachim (sic) Hill, trudging along on his little brown mare, a sheep-skin for a saddle and a small supply of tools for repairing clocks. His methods were primitive but effective—removing the works and boiling them in ashes and water being the cleaning process; the oil, a hickory nut pit held between heated tongs and over the desired parts until the proper results were accomplished."

It was a characteristic of Joakim Hill, as a repairman, to inscribe his name and the date of repair with white chalk and in script on the inside of the door of the clock case. The writer has seen two such examples of this trait of Hill's, once in a Morgan Hollinshead clock and again in a Brokaw clock. Hill wrote his name out fully. Of the dozen or so Joakim Hill clocks seen by the writer none had the evidences of hand crafting of the earlier makers—Pearson, Miller, or early Brokaws. All of the Hill clocks seen had the Moon Phase dials, rack and snail strike, and other characteristics of the type built from parts supplied "in the rough" by the machine shops of England. This is not to deprecate Hill's ability or skill as a clockmaker. It took a clockmaker to finish off these parts, make them fit each other, and end up with a functional piece of machinery. This was no mere job of assembly of prefabricated parts.

HILL, PETER, *Burlington*, 1796–1802. Carl Williams mentions in his book, *Silversmiths of New Jersey 1700–1825*, "In his 'Annuals' in 1869 Dr. Zachariah Reed wrote that (Hill's) shop was on the west side of Main Street near Mill Street. Records of the Quaker cemetery in Burlington mention a Peter Hill, a Negro, who learned the trade of watch and clockmaking." The Peter Hill in Mount Holly was a white man.

HILL, PETER, *Mount Holly*. De Cou wrote in *The Historic Rancocas* that "Miss Mary Deacon of Mount Holly has a tall clock, maker unknown, with the marking 'Cleaned by Peter Hill in 1803'."

HOLLINSHEAD, GEORGE, *Woodstown*. Born 1776. Died 1820. Son of Morgan. Moved when a young man to Woodstown from Moores Town. He was married to Hannah Scull Davis and occupied property belonging to his father-in-law, David Davis, at the northeast corner of Main Street and Bowen Avenue in Woodstown. Eight acres of land adjoining this property on the northeast was owned by Hollinshead at the time of his death. George Hollinshead, as did others of his family who were clockmakers, numbered his clocks. How many he actually made is not known, number 284 was sold about 1817. His clocks sold for about $100.00 depending on the quality of the case.

HOLLINSHEAD, HUGH, *Mount Holly*. Born 1753. Died 1786. According to inscriptions seen on the dials, Hugh Hollinshead made clocks in both Mount Holly and in Morris Town. Married to Elinor French in 1775. He was a cousin of Morgan. Shop and store on the southwest corner of Main Street and Old Evesham Road in Chester Township.

HOLLINSHEAD, HUGH JR., *Moorestown*. Born 1786, death date not known. May have made clocks, but none are known at this time.

HOLLINSHEAD, JACOB, *Salem*. Born 1747. Death date not known. Son of Joseph, had shop in Salem.

HOLLINSHEAD, JOB, *Haddonfield*. About 1820. Business taken over by John Whitehead in 1821.

HOLLINSHEAD, JOHN, *Burlington* and *Mount Holly*. Born 1745. Son of Joseph, Sr. Two clocks known, one of which is inscribed "John Hollinshead, Burlington" on a painted iron dial.

HOLLINSHEAD, JOSEPH SR., *Burlington*. The first New Jersey Hollinsheads, the grandparents of Joseph Sr., arrived in Salem in 1677. They came from Hollins in the Township of Sutton, Chester (England). In 1682 they moved to Burlington. Joseph Hollinshead (not yet senior) learned the clockmaking trade from Isaac Pearson. He married Pearson's daughter Sarah on May 5, 1740 and thereupon also became his partner. "Pearson and Hollinshead" clocks are known in some quantity, considering that they were handcrafted, and that Pearson had "other irons in the fire" besides clockmaking. The earliest clock with the inscription "Joseph Hollinshead" alone is 1755. There was no issue from the marriage of Joseph and Sarah

Clock of Joseph Hollinshead, Sr. Courtesy of the Monmouth County Historical Association.

Dial of the Joseph Hollinshead, Sr. clock.

Hollinshead. Upon his re-marriage, to Martha Howe, Joseph became the father of John, Samuel, Joseph Jr. and William.

In the accompanying photograph an oddity will be noted in that the dial is made of two separate pieces, the square part of the dial is apart from the lunette. The dial is very thin and hand hammered. The spandrels, chapter ring, and medallion on which his name is inscribed are all of pewter. There is no record of Hollinshead following in the footsteps of Isaac Pearson as a silversmith, although he did follow his example as a public figure. He was at one time Sheriff of Burlington County and was also a member of the West Jersey Proprietors in 1762.

HOLLINSHEAD, JOSEPH, JR., *Burlington.* Born 1751 and working in the 1770's and 1780's. He worked with his brother John. The clock shown is one of the few known with the names of the Hollinshead brothers, Joseph, Jr. and John, on the dial. The cabinetmaker is not known. The case is quite a bit more elaborate than the average New Jersey case. The entire pediment is more elaborate and other characteristics, the turnings of the columns in the hood, the door terminating in a fan design, the fluted quarter columns in the trunk and the base, and the graceful tulip design inlaid in the door leads one to believe that the case was made either in Philadelphia or by one trained to that type of cabinet work. The case is of walnut and it stands 7 feet 11 inches high.

HOLLINSHEAD, MORGAN, *Moorestown.* The frontispiece of De Cou's book *Moorestown and Her Neighbors* is a picture of one of Morgan Hollinshead's clock. This clock has Morgan Hollinshead's name inscribed on the dial and the location "Chester" which was the name of the area before it became known as Moorestown. It is therefore one of his very earliest. Other clocks known are his Nos. 34, 55, 70, 96, 104, and 107. All are with painted iron dials without moon phases. Morgan Hollinshead married Rebecca Matlack in 1775. He owned property east of the Friends Meeting House in Moorestown. He died there in 1832.

HOOLEY, RICHARD, *Flemington.* 1795–1840. Used painted iron dials with the Osborne intermediate plate. Three clocks known about in the Flemington area.

HOWELL, CHARLES, *Trenton.* 1820's–1830's.

Clock of Joseph, Jr. and John Hollinshead of Burlington. This clock is one of
the few with the names of the Hollinshead brothers on the dial. These brothers
were the sons of Joseph, Sr. who was
apprenticed to and later partner of Isaac
Pearson.

Clock of Morgan Hollinshead of Chester (now known as Moorestown). This clock carries the number 2, apparently the second one made by him. Owned by Mr. and Mrs. William H. Evans of Marlton.

Dial of the Morgan Hollinshead clock shown in the previous photograph.

Clock of Morgan Hollinshead. The number on this clock was obliterated by too thorough cleaning.

Dial of the Morgan Hollinshead clock shown in the previous photograph.

HOWELL, SILAS, *New Brunswick*. Born 1770. Advertised as "Clock and Watch Maker, Gold and Silversmith in *The Guardian* or *New Brunswick Advertiser*. Sold business to Charles Wheeler and Isaac Reed in 1798.

HUDSON, EDWARD, *Mount Holly*. Two clocks known. They are typical English design with rack and snail strike, painted iron dial, etc. The early 1800's is the nearest we were able to date Hudson's work.

HUDSON, WILLIAM, *Mount Holly*. This is the Hudson of the makers "Wood and Hudson" found on a clock dial. They were in business together about 1790 to 1810.

HURTIN and BIRGI, *Bound Brook*. 1766–1780. William Hurtin and Frederick Birgi were partners in what appears to be a jewelry and repair type of shop. Hurtin was primarily a silversmith while Birgi was the clock and watchmaker. The name Hurtin was used by the family after 1765. Previous to this date it was spelled Huertin. The Hurtin of this partnership was known as William Huertin III. He was a son of William Huertin, also a silversmith, of Newark and New York.

HUSSEY, M. L. M., *Menlo Park*. Patent No. 413,281, 1889, Electric Pendulum Driven Clock.

HUSTON, JAMES, *Trenton*. Early 1800's. Was employed in the shop of John Probasco. He made the first public clock in Trenton. It was installed in the steeple of the First Presbyterian Church and later at the City Hall. This is about 1805–06. He died in Montreal, Canada in 1822.

JACK, *Bound Brook*. Before 1780. This is a name found compounded with that of Lane (Aaron) on a clock dial. The whole inscription reads, "Lane & Jack, Bound Brook." The clock is located in the office of the president of Brown University and can be fairly dated by its history. The donor of the clock was James Manning. Manning was born in Elizabeth Town in 1738, attended the Baptist school in Hopewell in 1756, and graduated from Princeton University in 1762. He was a pastor in Scotch Plains until 1764, then a pastor in Warren, Rhode Island, 1765 to 1770, then went to Providence where he founded Brown University. It can be well imagined that the clock was a bit of home that he brought with him. The clock has a three-train movement, originally musical (the musical train is now missing except for the main wheel). The case is of "tiger striped" maple.

Clock of Edward Hudson of Mount Holly.

JEROME, CHAUNCY. At work in New Jersey for several months as a cabinetmaker making cases for tall clocks. The following is from his *History of the American Clock Business For The Past Sixty Years and The Life of Chauncy Jerome Written by Himself.**

"Having got myself tolerably well posted about clocks in Waterbury, I hired myself to two men, Messrs. Hotchkiss and Pierpont, to go into the State of New Jersey, to make the old fashioned seven-foot standing clock cases. They had been selling that kind of clock without the cases in the northern part of that state for about twenty dollars apiece. The purchasers had complained to them however that there was no one in that region that could make the case for them, which prevented many others from buying. These two men whom I went with, told them that they would get someone to go out from Connecticut to make the case, and thought they could be made for about eighteen or twenty dollars apiece, which would make the whole clock cost about forty dollars—not so costly after all; for a clock was then considered the most useful of anything that could be had in a family, for what it cost.

"I entered into an agreement with these men at once and a few days after we three started on the 14th Dec., 1812, with provisions for the journey, to the far off Jersey . . .

"On crossing the Hudson from New York, it was the first time that I had ever crossed a stream excepting on a bridge, I feared that we might upset and all be drowned; but no accident happened to us; we landed in safety and went on our way rejoicing towards Elizabeth Town . . . We passed through Elizabeth Town and Morristown to Dutch Valley where we stopped for the night. We remained at this place a few days, looking for a cabinet shop, or a suitable place, to make the clock cases. Not succeeding we went a mile further north, to a place called Schooler's† Mountain; here we found a building that suited us. It was then the day before Christmas . . . A young man from the lower part of New Jersey worked with me all winter . . . We would work on the average of fifteen hours a day, the housework not occupying much of our time. I was then only nineteen years old . . . We worked in this way all winter. When the job was finished, I took my little budget of clothes and started for home. I travelled the first day as far as Elizabeth Town and stopped there all night."

The sophisticated cabinetmaker of the day who, because he took the opportunity to advertise or was proud to put his name on his work, frequently pasted within the clock case his name and place of business. There are no known Chauncy Jerome cases. Neither have

---

*Published by F. C. Dayton, Jr., 1860.

†Apparent misspelling of Schooley's Mountain.

there been found any clocks with the names Hotchkiss and Pierpont on them. Brooks Palmer in his book, *The Book of American Clocks*, mentions Hotchkiss and Pierpont as of Plymouth, Connecticut about 1810. He does not identify them as either makers or sellers.

Since Jerome was so young, nineteen, when he made clock cases in New Jersey, we can assume that they were not of the caliber of the more experienced artisans of the time. Also, we can believe that they were made of local woods, the fruit woods or pine.

JOHNSON, JOHN, *Hightstown*. 1850–51. In *Kirkbride's Directory*.

JOHNSON, JOHN, *Morristown*. 1850–51. In *Kirkbride's Directory*.

KESSELMEIER, FREDERICK, *Newark*. In *Newark Directory*, 1835–36, "Watch and Clock Maker, 156 Broad."

KING, G. W., *Morristown*. 1850–51. In *Kirkbride's Directory*.

KROEBER, F., *Hoboken*. Patent No. 152,292, 1874, Clock Clockwork Attachment, Patent No. 180,138, 1876, Clock, Patent No. 184,972, 1876, Clock Movement, and Patent No. 193,663, 1877, Calendar Clock Dial.

KRUEGER, ADOLF, *Camden*. 1850–1862.

LA FOY, THEODORE, *Newark*. 1848–1852.

LANE & JACK, *Bound Brook*. See discussion under Jack.

LANE, AARON, *Elizabeth Town* and *Bound Brook*. Born 1753. Died 1819. Most of what is known about Lane is from the many advertisements of his found in old newspapers, also the public announcements made in the newspapers of his activities as an attorney, auditor, administrator of estates, and as a "receiver." Lane's many activities included that of Justice of the Peace, Alderman (under Elizabeth Town's first mayor, John De Hart) merchant, silversmith and maker of fine clocks.

The first advertisement known of Aaron Lane is found in the files of the *New Jersey Journal* of April 25, 1780:

"This is to inform the public that the subscriber has removed to Williams Farms, two miles from Elizabeth Town, on the road to Westfield, where he continues to carry on the silversmiths business, and will endeavor to give all that satisfaction to those gentlemen and ladies who are pleased to favour him with their custom, that lays in his power.

Aaron Lane"

Between 1780 and 1815 Lane advertised many times. Dr. Theodore Thayer, in his excellent book, "*As We Were—The Story of Old Elizabeth-Town*" noted that "Aaron Lane's store and silversmith's shop was next East of the White house. By 1815 wood and coal stoves were coming into general use. Aaron Lane carried a full line of stoves, stove pipe and sheet iron."

Before leaving the consideration of Lane's general endeavors and adhering to his clockmaking, let us here note that one of his shops operated under the name of Lane and Will. A clock was found in Rhode Island (see Jack) which has inscribed on the dial, "Lane and Jack." Here is the oddity that in two separate cases, Lane's name is combined with another and *each* of the others is what is commonly used as a first name of the male gender—Will and Jack. It is not impossible, of course, that these were the surname of individuals, but some extensive research to determine whether this was so, and to know who they were has been fruitless.

Of the 15 clocks found made by Aaron Lane, four were inscribed, "Bound Brook." This would indicate that Lane's greater activity in clockmaking was in Elizabeth Town, although further research might refute that. Their dials are of brass quite expertly engraved, not only with the maker's name and location, but with flowerlets and leaves. The engraving is so consistent in character and quality as to indicate that it all was done by Lane himself. The design of the movements are in general consistent, with the exception of the two musical clocks known.

One dial was found to be somewhat different. The calendar aperture was a square, just below the arbors on which the hands are mounted. The maker's name was inscribed on an arched band reaching across the dial from the numerals eight to four. The seconds chapter ring was in the normal position of the upper center part of the dial. The medallion in the lunette where usually we find the maker's name is there, but it serves as the location of a small lever that is moved to one of two positions, Strike and Silent, to control the striking of the clock.

The cases of the Lane clocks were found to be variously made of walnut, cherry, and mahogany. They varied sufficiently in style as to indicate that not all were made by the same cabinetmaker. The cabinet work in all was good.

An outstanding record of New Jersey craftsmanship is the Lane clock owned by H. Kels Swan of South Bound Brook. We found many clocks that were apparently of New Jersey origin, but they had no means of identification. This clock of Mr. Swan's has not only the name Aaron Lane on the dial and the name Ichabod Williams on

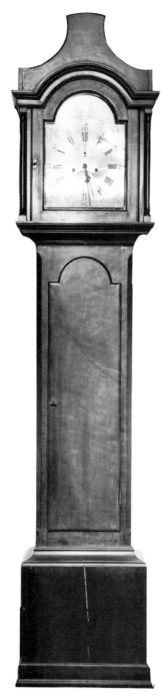

Clock of Aaron Lane of Elizabeth Town.
Owned by H. Kels Swan of South Bound
Brook.

Dial of the Aaron Lane clock shown in the previous photograph.
The hands are replacements of the originals.

Ichabod Williams label found in the case of a Lane clock. Williams was Aaron Lane's brother-in-law.

Dial of another Aaron Lane clock. It is characteristic of Lane's dials that such embellishment found on them are engravings, flowerlets, and leaves with graceful curving stems, where spandrels are found on other dials. In the lunette are delicate scrolls reminiscent of those found in the old Palmer method school texts on penmanship. Owned by Karl Jacobi of Chatham.

the label within the case, but also the repair date and repairman's name, Joakim Hill, written in script with white chalk, inside the door of the case! Truly this is a New Jersey clock. The burial records of the First Presbyterian Church in Elizabeth recorded of Lane's death, "Aaron Lane, Esq. Age 66, October 25, 1819. Disease: Decay of nature."

LANE, MARK, *Elizabeth Town*. 1822. The writer has seen and inspected to some degree twelve clocks with labels imprinted "Made and Sold By Mark Lane." These were all shelf clocks with wooden movements, mostly mahogany plates. The use of mahogany plates may have been the "Improvement" Lane mentions on his labels, although he also mentions that the clocks were made under the Terry Patent. The labels seen in different clocks were found to be mostly of Southington (Connecticut). Some of these were overpasted with another label giving Elizabeth Town as the origin. Two clocks were found that had the origin of the clock as Elizabeth Town which were not overpasted, but original.

Unhappily no business address, advertisement, or other similar indication that Mark Lane was a clockmaker was found. The only mention at all of him as a clockmaker was found in Dr. Thayer's *As We Were—The Story of Old Elizabeth Town*, in the instance where Mark Lane competed with Samuel Kennedy Miller for the job of repairing the town clock. (See Miller, Samuel Kennedy). Here, too, it might be considered that Lane might have been interested in getting the job and then "subcontracting" it elsewhere. Only the genealogical history learned about of Southington, Connecticut indicated a trade for Mark Lane and that reference mentions him as cabinet-maker. It would seem that with the knowledge at hand, at this time, that Lane assembled the component parts of wood movement shelf clocks, but made none.

On one of the Mark Lane clocks owned by Edward N. C. Davis of Rosemont, was found a dial which gives evidence that this was Lane's own family clock. In each of the four corners was found, written in script, the name of each of his first four children. Between the double lines that are the perimeter of the chapter ring was also found some writing. The words in themselves are quite legible, but put together their meaning is somewhat obscure. The label in this clock is an overpaste of Elizabeth Town, N.J. over Southington, Conn.

LAWSE, JONATHON, *Amwell*. 1788-1809. Also spelled Laashe and Lawshe. Two clocks known.

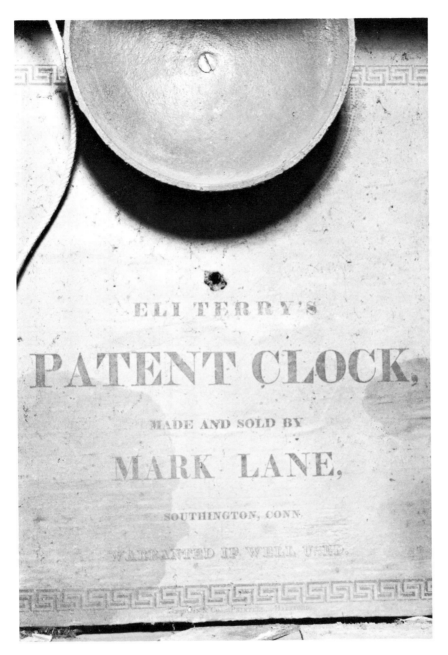

Label of a Mark Lane clock found in the Flemington area. This is an example of the Southington, Connecticut designation. Courtesy of Edward N. C. Davis of Rosemont.

Label from another Mark Lane clock having an overpaste of "Elizabeth-Town, N. J." placed over the original Southington designation. Courtesy of Edward N. C. Davis of Rosemont.

Shelf clock by Mark Lane. Owned by Alfred Butler of Hope.

Label in Mark Lane's shelf clock showing a different type of Lane's overpasting.

Facsimile of dial of what was apparently Mark Lane's family clock. It carries the names of his first four children in the four corners, plus written material around the chapter ring.

LAWSHE, JOHN, *Amwell Township*. About 1750. One clock known. In the *New Jersey History of Marriages* is mention of a John Lawshe being married to Penelope Chamberline, September 3, 1779.

LESLIE, WILLIAM J., *New Brunswick* and *Trenton*. Partner with Henry Gaither in 1814, later, before 1798 with Benjamin Williams. Advertised that he "Was not from London, Paris or Boston but a native of New Jersey." In 1799 Leslie and his partner Williams moved to Trenton on Warren Street in the shop previously owned by Joseph Yates, clockmaker, who moved to another part of town. About 1805 Leslie worked alone. He moved again in 1817 and became a tavernkeeper. His business was taken over by Hugh Ely, another clockmaker. The activities as a tavernkeeper brought to a close Leslie's career as a clockmaker. He subsequently was occupied in the operation of the Phoenix Hotel on Warren Street in 1821, then in 1824 the Mansion House also on Warren Street. This was called the Temperance Inn in deference to the temperance furor in the 1830's.

In 1803 Leslie married Ann Vandegrift, of Trenton. His career also embraced the duties of Town Marshal 1807–08 and City Assessor in 1808–10. He died November 30, 1831 at the age of 62.

LESLIE (WILLIAM) AND WILLIAMS (BENJAMIN), *New Brunswick* and *Trenton*. Several clocks are known including a fine specimen in the Monmouth County Historical Society, a musical clock in an Egerton, Jr. case. In 1803 they took over the shop of Yates and Kent in Trenton.

LEWIS, ISAAC, *Newark*. On August 28, 1782, the *New Jersey Journal* carried the following advertisement, "Isaac Lewis Informs the publick that he has opened a shop in Newark, where he carries on the Clock and Watch Makers business in its different branches:—Likewise all kinds of Silversmith's work and engraving in the best manner. Any Ladies or Gentlemen who please to favour him with their custom, may depend on being served with expedition and upon reasonable terms. August 27, 1772."

LORD, JAMES, *Woodbury*. 1821–1835.

LOW, ALEXANDER, *New Brunswick*. Low came from Scotland in 1774. In 1788 he married Anne Davis, a granddaughter of Robert Rhea who was also a cabinetmaker of Freehold. Low made cases for Leslie and Williams, a fine specimen of which is owned by a great, great grandson of his, Charles E. Moreau of Montclair. This case is of cherry wood and done in the Chippendale style.

WILLIAM J. LESLIE,
Clock & Watch-Maker,

[Not from London, Paris or Boston, but a *Native of New-Jersey*]

LIKE other *Patriots* of the day, continues to offer his services to the Public for *Love* and *Money*, at the OLD STAND next door north of the INDIAN QUEEN TAVERN, Trenton. With sincere acknowledgments for past favours he hopes for additional claims on his gratitude by his Fellow-Jerseymen, in the honor of whose service he is ever ambitious to exert his '*energies.*' Being attached by *nature* and *habit* to the old fashioned way of living by *eating* and *drinking*, he feels disposed to accomodate his Country Friends with the Goods and Wares of his Manufactory in exchange for many of those *Comforts of Life* with which the bounty of Providence has crowned their labours in the early and later Harvest. He has now on hand, devoted to the *good of the People*,

THE FOLLOWING ARTICLES:

GOLD WATCHES, plain, and with day of the month.
SILVER DITTO, first quality.
CHIME CLOCKS
PLAIN DITTO, with Mohogany, Cherry and Black Walnut Cases.
FUZEE CHAIN HOOKS and CHAINS.
PENDANT and Bows.
MAIN SPRINGS
CASE SPRINGS and BUTTONS
GOLD HANDS.
GILT DITTO.
STEEL DITTO.
CLOCK DIALS.
WATCH CHAINS, SEALS and KEYS.
WATCH GLASSES of all sizes from No 8 to No. 40.
CLOCK GUT
EIGHT-DAY forg'd work and PINIONS.
EIGHT-DAY CASTINGS.

The above Goods are offered to the Public on moderate Terms; and through it may be unnecessary to multiply words in their favour, the Subscriber will just observe, that his CLOCKS and WATCHES, beside the mere use of informing their Possessors what o' the clock at morn, noon or even, or through the "unguarded hours of night" are excellent *monitors* to the *sluggard* and the *drone*, and those who kill time in idleness or dissipation—They also afford encouraging example to persevering industry, in exhibiting what may be performed by steady and unremitted toil. By them likewise the discreet Housewife is enabled so to time the concerns of Domestic Economy, that all things may work together for good, and the "savory meal" be seasonably prepared for the "mouth of labour" and to fill the hungry with good things—matters of high concern in preserving "harmony with *family* intercourse," without which "*liberty* and even *life* are but dreary things."

CLOCKS and WATCHES cleaned and repaired on the shortest Notice and in the best manner—All orders punctually executed, and every favour duly acknowledged.

N. B. Wanted at the above mentioned Business TWO APPRENTICES. Boys from the country will be preferred.

Trenton, January 28, 1805.   9 3w

Clever satirical advertisement of William J. Leslie. It gives a philosophical dissertation of how men and women could and should use the time that his watches and clocks measured for them. It appeared in the *Trenton Federalist* on January 28, 1805.

Leslie and Williams musical clock with the case made by Matthew Egerton, Jr. (his label is inside the door). The dial is inscribed with the names of the tunes that the clock plays: Banks of the Dee; Nancy Dawson; Merry Dance, Quaker; Successful Campaign; and Rakes of Marlow. Courtesy of Monmouth County Historical Association.

Dial of the Leslie and Williams musical clock shown in the previous photograph.

Leslie and Williams clock in a cherry wood case by Alexander Low. Owned by Charles E. Moreau of Montclair.

Leslie and Williams musical clock in an apparent Egerton case. The tunes, varying from those of the other musical clock are: Bunker Hill, Indian Chief, Yankee Doodle, Tink-a-Tank, Banks ('o) the Dee, and Danville. The melody plays the tune to which the indicator points every three hours. Courtesy of Henry Ford Museum, Dearborn, Michigan.

Front of movement of Leslie and Williams musical clock. The cup-shaped piece at top center of the movement with its stepped edge determines the tune to be played. The cylinder is of wood clad with a sheet of brass and holds the pins that trip the hammers. This is identical to the well known "Swiss" music boxes.

Rear of musical clock movement. The rack at the lower left has four teeth. This and other evidences within the movement indicate that the original design of the clock caused the music to be played each quarter hour. The many repairers' hands through which this clock passed altered this.

LUPP, HARVEY, (Also spelled Leupp and Loop), *New Brunswick*. 1809–1815. The Lupps, as we shall spell their name, were active mostly in silversmithing. Those who had anything to do with clocks we here mention.

LUPP, HENRY, *New Brunswick*. About 1785. Advertised for sale an eight-day town clock made by him on Albany Street. He was primarily a silversmith. He was born in 1760. His death date is not known.

LUPP, JOHN, *New Brunswick*. Born 1734. Died 1805. Willed tools, shop furniture, and shop timepiece to son William who succeeded him in 1805.

LUPP, PETER, *New Brunswick*. One of three brothers, others were John and Christian, who arrived in New Jersey before 1760. Peter was a silversmith and clockmaker. Carl Williams has recorded several pieces of silver of Peter Lupp in his book, *Silversmiths of New Jersey 1700–1825*. One of Lupp's fine clocks is herein illustrated. It is located in the Buccleuch Mansion, Buccleuch Park, New Brunswick. The movement is conventional. The case is of cherry about 8 feet tall. The caliber of workmanship in the unidentified case could be that of either Parsell or Egerton. The inlay work is particularly good.

The will of Peter Lupp, dated May 12, 1802 (inventory March 30, 1807), identifies him as a clockmaker.

LUPP, WILLIAM, *New Brunswick*. Son of John, he succeeded his father in business in 1805. Only clock work known was his charge of the town clock, this by appointment according to his account books of 1801–1827.

MARSH, OLIVER B., *Newark*. Listed in the *Newark City Directories* from 1855–1875. The directory for 1876 listed him, "Oliver B. Marsh, Binghamton, New York." Oddly, the directory for 1880 again mentions, "O. B. Marsh, Watches and Clocks, Binghamton, New York." While in Newark, Marsh spent three and a half years making the very handsome clock illustrated here. He took it with him when he moved to Binghamton and displayed it in the jewelry store he established there.

In a pamphlet *Industries of Binghamton* written in 1892, Marsh's clock was described as follows: "The elaborately ornamented and perfectly finished marble clock which attracts the attention of all who pass the show windows of his store was entirely made by him and is as perfect an example of horological skill as was ever produced either in this country or abroad."

Clock of Peter Lupp of New Brunswick. One of the more rare clocks of a fine craftsman of New Jersey. The case is of cherry wood richly inlaid with holly or satin wood. Beautifully crafted by an artisan in wood. Courtesy of the Buccleuch Restoration Committee and Mrs. Joseph H. Kler.

Dial of the Peter Lupp clock shown in the previous photograph.

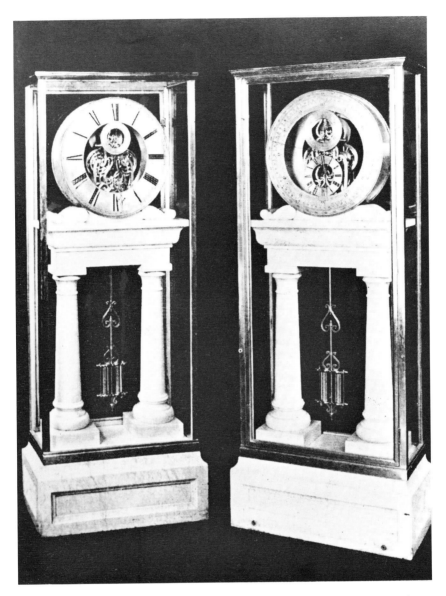

Clock by Oliver B. Marsh. The view on the right is the front of
the clock and that on the left is the rear. Courtesy of the Hagans
Clock Manor Museum, Orville R. Hagans, Curator.

The overall dimensions of the Marsh clock are 68 inches high, 26 inches wide and 12 inches deep. The clock weighs 1000 pounds. The lyre-shaped movement is of bronze, with the pinions of highly polished steel. In the movement are 10 ruby and 20 sapphire jewels. the escapement, indigenous to the maker, has two sets of pallets working off the single escape wheel—one set, the locking and the other, the impulse. The locking stones are set the opposite from the ordinary clock and the locking corner is also the let-off corner. Hand cast lead weights power the clock, descending down the hollowed marble columns. The pendulum is mercury compensating. There are two large dials, one on either side, 18 inches in diameter. There are two small dials within the front large dial and one small dial within the large dial in the rear. The front side of the clock tells the hours, minutes, seconds, days of the year, months, and dates. The rear of the clocks tells the hours, minutes, and seconds.

Having been lost, the pendulum has been replaced magnificently. The present pendulum was designed by Kenneth E. Washburn, Professor of Fine Arts at Cornell University. Rex E. Moore of Phoenix, Arizona came into possesion of the clock in 1939 and spent six years repairing it.

There are nine screw adjustments on the escapement. It is so well constructed and its adjustments so exacting that the clock will run within a few seconds a year. After more than fifty years of running there are no signs of wear.

The Marsh clock described above is now part of the outstanding collection owned by the Hagans Clock Manor Museum in Evergreen, Colorado. The Curator is Orville R. Hagans, and the Director is Mrs. Orville R. Hagans. The details of construction of the Marsh clock are from *American Horologist and Jeweler,* December 1949.

MASON, P., *Somerville,* 1842. Interesting label advertising his "Fancy Store," in a shelf clock owned by Aaron Johnson of Pluckemin. The design and work marks on the movement show originality and hand crafting. There are no identifying marks on the movement.

MASON, WILLIAM H., *Mount Holly.* 1834–1861. De Cou mentions in *The Historic Rancocas* a tall clock with the inscription of Mason on the dial in Mount Holly.

Label in a shelf clock owned by Aaron Johnson of Pluckemin. It is questionable, to say the least, to say judging from the nature of the label that P. Mason was a clockmaker.

Strap movement of rather different design in the "P. Mason clock."

MAUS, JACOB, *Trenton.* Advertised in Trenton in the 1780's. Was first located at the corner of Broad and State Streets. In 1782 Maus was located at the corner of Queen and Second Streets, then in 1784 he moved to Warren Street opposite the Indian King Tavern north of the original site of the Indian Queen. Jacob Maus had a son Frederick, a clockmaker in Philadelphia. In 1786, Frederick was paid 264.2.3 from the inventory of his father of 1785, this in account of Job Rozell.

MIDDLETON, AARON, *Burlington.* Apprenticed to Isaac Pearson and ran away in 1732.

MIDDLETON, AARON HEWES, *Woodbury.* One clock known marked "Woodberry." It is not known whether he was a descendant of the Burlington, Aaron Middleton who found servitude with Isaac Pearson not to his liking. He died intestate in Evesham Township, Burlington County, June 27, 1800.

MILLER, AARON, *Elizabeth Town.* One of the earliest New Jersey clockmakers, preceded only by Isaac Pearson of Burlington. His first advertisement appeared in the *New York Gazette* on November 16, 1747. The same advertisement appeared in the same paper November 23, 30; December 6, 14, 21, 28 and January 4, 1748.

All of Aaron Miller's efforts were as a craftsman and artisan. He left no evidence that he was interested, as many other New Jersey clockmakers did, in public affairs. His only involvement with governmental procedures was the time when he exercised his mechanical ability and competed with the government in fashioning coins from molds and dies of his making. It was called counterfeiting.

Of Miller's improvement in a compass, Benjamin Franklin was moved to write from London in 1765, "an ingenious man in the Province of New Jersey." No small praise considering it came from one of the most ingenious men of all time.

In his brass foundry Miller cast his clock works, as perhaps the clock works for others, his instruments, and bells. He taught several his trade or trades. One was David Ross, his apprentice and helper in the foundry in 1760. Together with Ross, bells were made for public buildings in Amboy, Burlington, Hopewell, Millstone, Staten Island, and Woodbridge. He taught his son Cornelius and his, at first apprentice then later son-in-law, Isaac Brokaw to make clocks. In Isaac Brokaw he found a learner who, as far as clocks were concerned, outdid the master. This in the number of clocks evident today, not in any change in design or quality of workmanship in the movement.

Very early Aaron Miller clock. The case is of pine, painted and stenciled. The workmanship in the case while mechanically adequate, lacks the "air" of fine cabinet work. It could have been made by Aaron Miller himself. Courtesy of Edward J. Grassmann of Elizabeth.

Left side of the movement of the early Aaron Miller clock. Here can be seen qualities of design later carried out by all the Brokaws such as the wood winding drums, the count wheel of the strike train mounted between the plates, the simple striking mechanism, and the very thin hand-hammered brass in the dial.

Right side of the movement of the early Aaron Miller clock. Note the piece cut out of the upper right corner of the back plate. Why? Well, brass was hard to come by, and he needed a small piece. This area of the plate wasn't doing anything, so presto, here's a small piece of brass to use elsewhere!

Dial of the early Aaron Miller clock.

Aside from Miller's clocks, those of Brokaw's (and his son) there was found only one other that employed his design. The one other was the clock of Stephen Tichenor of Newark. The main feature of the Miller clocks is the count wheel, for the strike, to be between the plates and just before, but attached to the main wheel on the strike side.* Count wheels were used before and since Miller, but all others are seen mounted external to the plates. The older clocks of Europe had them almost always on the back plate. The New England wood works clocks have them on the front plate. Other qualities characteristic to Miller were, very thin hand-hammered brass dials, wooden winding drums, and a lifting lever in the striking mechanism

AARON MILLER, Clock-Maker,
In *Elizabeth* Town, Eaft-New-Jerfey;
MAKES and fells all Sorts of Clocks, after
the beft Manner, with Expedition :----He likewife makes Compaffes and Chains for Surveyors ; as alfo Church Bells of any fize, he having a Foundery for that Purpofe, and has caft feveral which have been approved to be good ; and will fupply any Perfons on a timely Notice, with any of the above Articles, at very reafonable Rates.

Advertisement of Aaron Miller in the *New York Gazette*, Revived in *The Weekly Post Boy*, January 4, 1748.

shaped like a horizontal streak of lightning. One very peculiar oddity seen on Miller's clocks, and a few of Isaac Brokaw's, is a piece cut off or out of the back plate. Why was this done? The reader may draw his own conclusion. That of the writer is that brass was very scarce in these days so Aaron Miller said to himself, "This brass isn't doing any thing here, I need a piece about that size, so I'll slice it off." Why did Isaac Brokaw slice pieces off the right rear corner of his back plates? Well, he was working at nearly the same time as Miller, and didn't he learn his trade and "tricks of the trade" from Miller?

Fire having destroyed almost all the records of the First Presbyterian Church on Broad Street in Elizabeth, there are no certain rec-

*A similar principle was employed by Benjamin Chandlee, using appropriately spaced pins located on the inner surface of the main wheel of the strike train, instead of a separate notched count wheel. Edward E. Chandlee, Six Quaker Clockmakers, p 232. David McKay Company, Philadelphia.

Aaron Miller clock in an oak case. Located at the Morristown National Historical Park.

Dial and hood of the Aaron Miller clock in the Morristown National Historical Park.

An Aaron Miller clock in a sugar pine case. The clock was at one time on exhibition at the Newark Museum.

Aaron Miller clock owned by H. Kels
Swan of South Bound Brook.

Dial of the Aaron Miller clock owned by H. Kels Swan of South
Bound Brook.

Aaron Miller clock. The glazed aperture in the door of the case afforded the gratification of seeing the pendulum in motion. Owned by Karl Jacobi of Chatham.

Dial of the Aaron Miller clock owned by Karl Jacobi of Chatham.

An Aaron Miller musical clock. Owned
by Edward J. Grassmann of Elizabeth.

Dial of the Aaron Miller musical clock owned by Edward J. Grassmann of Elizabeth. Note that the corner spandrels and those about the boss match in design.

Side of the movement of the Aaron Miller musical clock showing
the musical mechanism. The propellor-like appendage is the wind
vane that governs the speed at which the music is played. There is
no indication, as on the Leslie and Williams musical clock, that
this clock plays more than one tune. The clock was inoperable
when examined and photographed, so the playing of the music
could not be noted. We guess that but one tune is its complete
repertoire.

ords of who built the clock that was installed there in the spring of 1759. There was no other clockmaker in Elizabeth Town at that time, excepting Aaron Miller. It might not be unreasonable to assume that it was he who supplied it. Too, there was already a bell in the belfry of the church and again Miller being the only caster of bells in the area almost certainly cast and hung it there. People being then pretty much as they are today, logic dictates that Miller, "having his foot in the door" was given the work of making the clock. Evidence is certain that Miller serviced the clock. In the Nicholas Murray book, published in 1844 and titled, *Notes, Historical and Biographical Concerning Elizabeth-Town Its Eminent Men, Churches and Ministers*, is a reference to the Old First Presbyterian Church on Broad Street. It had a high steeple with a town clock in it, of which a Mr. Miller had the care for many years."

The cases for the clocks of Aaron Miller, though well made from a mechanic's point of view, are quite primitive in design. Most found were flat topped and of pine. Their quality and design has caused the writer to believe that Miller built them himself. They quite lack the air of grace that is possessed by the work of skilled cabinet makers.

Aaron Miller died in 1779.

MILLER, CORNELIUS, *Elizabeth Town*. Birth date not known. Died in 1779, the same year as his father, Aaron. Inherited with his brother-in-law, Isaac Brokaw, his father's clockmaking tools. His clocks heard about, but not seen by the writer. Had children Johanna, Elizabeth, Margaret, Sarah, Abigail and Aaron. Son Aaron and brother William were executors for his estate. Witnesses were John Brokaw (son of Isaac), William Barnet, and George Ross. The will was proved June 28, 1779. Jonathan Miller and Sarah Miller were administrators for the sale of Cornelius' belongings which were listed as "a clock, watch, compass-making tools, etc."

MILLER, KENNEDY, *Elizabeth Town*. Although this name appears in several listings of clockmakers, and one of silversmiths, the writer has found no other evidence that such an individual existed. It is probable that there has been some confusion with the name Samuel Kennedy Miller. People sometimes use their middle names for common usage retaining the given names for legal purposes only. It is true that an advertisement did appear headed "Kennedy Miller" (see illustration), it is true also that in the March 1931 issue of *Antiques* magazine, a "Kennedy Miler" (spelled with one l) was written about and pictured on pages 233 and 234, it is true also that in *Hutchinson's Bib-*

... Judging from the history of "Old First" Church, the edifices of its history have supported a town clock since 1724. The history, as written says: "In 1724 a new church, 42 by 58 feet, was erected, was afterward enlarged in 1766 to 74 by 42 feet. This building was

Bell in the tower of the First Presbyterian Church in Elizabeth.
Fire destroyed the church on June 25, 1946. Photograph was
made just after the fire and shows the bell hanging in the belfry
still supported by the charred timbers. It is quite possible, even
probable, that the bell was cast by Aaron Miller in Elizabeth
Town in about 1750 to 1760. Unfortunately, no records exist to
confirm this as they were all destroyed in the fire.

continued

burned by the British in 1780. It was quite a fine building, with
bell, steeple and clock.

The original part of the present edifice was commenced in 1784
and completed in 1789. The church building has been altered,
extended and improved many times. In 1899 the steeple was
demolished by a tornado and the original clock destroyed. The
present (1939) timepiece was set in the steeple in 1901.

It is interesting that many prominent citizens, of all churches
and beliefs, contributed to the fund that financed setting the
present clock.—*Elizabeth Daily Journal*, October 12, 1939.

Here the tower clock is shown being destroyed by fire, as was
the earlier clock. This fire, on June 25, 1946, also destroyed the
entire church. Photograph provided through the courtesy of *The
Daily Journal*, Elizabeth.

liography of New Jersey Names he mentions, "Kennedy Miller (sometimes called Canada)."

Diligent research, including the *Archives and Genealogies of New Jersey* has not revealed any "Kennedy Miller" "Canada Miller" or "Kennedy Miler." The writer is pretty well satisfied that Samuel Kennedy Miller, the grandson of Aaron Miller and son of Robert Miller, and Kennedy Miller, Canada Miller and Kennedy Miler were all the same person.

MILLER, SAMUEL KENNEDY, *Elizabeth Town.* Born 1777. Died 1850. Of the many Millers researched in and of Elizabeth Town, between 1750 and 1850, the only one found with a given name of Kennedy was Samuel Kennedy Miller. Samuel Kennedy Miller was a grandson of Aaron Miller. His father was Robert, his mother Sarah (Kennedy) Miller. He married Sarah Williams of Union. None of his six children had the name Kennedy. They were Anna, Eliza, Oliver Williams, (note the second given name here, that of his mother's maiden name, *just as his* father was given his mother's maiden name), Hannah, Adeline and William Washburn. All were baptized in the First Presbyterian Church in Elizabethtown.

In *As We Were—The Story of Old Elizabethtown* Dr. Thayer wrote,

KENNEDY MILLER,
CLOCK-MAKER,
AND
GOLD & SILVER SMITH.

INFORMS his friends and the public, that he carries on the above branches in all their variety, at his Shop, near this Printing-Office. The SILVER PLATING busineſs he alſo carries on—Furniture for Harneſs, Carriage Springs, &c. &c. warranted as well done, and at as low rates as thoſe imported.

Wanted Immediately.

A BOY, 14 or 15 years of age, as an Apprentice to the above branches of buſineſs.
Eliz. Town, April 25, 1803. 14 4w

"As amusing as it was typical of the times was the way the town fathers handled the matter of repairing the town clock on the Court House in 1822. Samuel Miller, a local clockmaker, offered to repair the clock, but Mark Lane, another clockmaker, convinced the Common Council that it would be better to have a new one made. Thereupon the Council voted to have Lane make the clock. The decision was not well received by the townspeople. Lane was then informed that the town fathers had reconsidered and decided against having him make a new clock. The question was finally settled when the Common Council voted to have the clock repaired for $200.00, by a New York clockmaker."

At the Executor's sale of Samuel Miller's estate his tools identified him as a clockmaker. The notice read, "Executor's Sale, Will be sold Feb. 25, 1851 at the late residence (North Broad Street) of Samuel K. Miller, deceased, the personal property of said deceased consisting of sundry articles, viz: 6 brass clocks, 1 pr. blacksmith's bellows, 2 turn-lathes, 1 pr. plater's rollers iron vices (sic), coach handles and bands,a lot of files and a variety of clockmaker's and plater's tools. Dated 2–18–1851."

MORRIS, William, *Bridgeton* and *Camden*. At Bridgeton in 1811, and moved to Camden in 1831.

MULFORD, ABRAHAM MARSH, *Elizabeth Town*. Cabinetmaker, partner of Abraham Rosett. See Rosett & Mulford.

MULFORD, N. E., *Madison*. Patent No. 77,080, Striking Attachment for Clocks.

NEWARK CLOCK COMPANY, *Newark*. Listed in *Newark Directory*, 1926–1941. "Pres-Treas., Frederick H. Spitzhoff h. Mountainside."

NEWTON, J. L., *New Brunswick*. Advertisement in *The Guardian* or *New Brunswick Advertiser* December 14, 1803, "I. L. Newton, Watch and Clockmaker. Has removed to Mr. John Voorhees, upper end of Albany Street, two doors above the printing office, where he carries on the Watch and Clockmaking business in their various branches. Any gentleman who may choose to employ him, may depend on having his commands attended to, and executed with neatness and dispatch, and the least favour gratefully acknowledged. N. B. All kinds of Clocks and Watches repaired, warranted for one year."

NICHOLL, JAMES, *Belvidere*. Listed in *Kirkbride's Directory*, 1850–51.

Clock of William Morris of Bridgeton.
The case is of walnut, eight feet tall.
Courtesy of Earl Strickler of Columbia,
Pennsylvania.

Dial and hood of the William Morris clock.

REMOVAL.

WILLIAM MORRIS,
CLOCK AND WATCH MAKER.

Has removed from Bridgeton, to the city of
Camden, N. J. opposite the Court House,
where he intends carrying on the *Clock and
Watch Making Business*, in all its branches,
and having served a regular apprenticeship
and followed the business upwards of 20
years in Bridgeton, N. J. now solicits the in-
habitants of Camden, and the public in general, for a share of public patronage, and
hopes by a due attention to business to merit
a share of public favor, and to all those that
will favor him with their custom, no exertion
on his part shall be wanting to give general satisfaction,

N B. He keeps for sale Clocks, Watches, Chains, Keys, Seals, &c. &c. which he
will sell as cheap as in Philadelphia.

May, 7, 1831.—tf.

Advertisement of William Morris. Courtesy of Rutgers University Library of
Special Collections.

NICHOLL, JOHN, *Belvidere.* 1790–1818. The name on the clock dial
seen has the spelling of the first name abbreviated "JN°" which the
writer presumes to be John. Aside from the unusual, in terms of today's spelling, printing of the first name on the dial, the rest is also
different. The location Belvidere is followed by the letters W, C, just
below Belvidere and in the center. We can assume that these letters,
in spite of the commas used, are the dial painter's abbreviation for
Warren County, which contains Belvidere.

Examination of the movement causes the writer to believe that this
clock of Nicholl's was designed by him. This in spite of the similarity
between this clock and that found of John Parke of Paterson. Both
are designed for a sweep seconds hand, but each is different from the
other in the location of the wheels to effect this. The dial of the
Nicoll's clock varies too in that it has a chapter ring painted on it for
the days of the month, a rather large decorative brass hand is used as
the indicator for this. A false or intermediate plate is used to attach
the dial to the clock, again examination indicated that the plate was
made by Nicholl. It is not the usual fairly heavy cast iron of Osborne
or Wilson, with either of their names cast into it, it is comparatively
thin and seems to be of wrought iron. There is no name on it. It ap-

Clock of John Nicholl of Belvidere. Courtesy of the Newark Museum.

Dial of the John Nicholl clock. The inner chapter ring is for the calender hand to indicate the days of the month. The longest hand is the sweep second hand. Having four hands, with their pivotal point at the center of the dial, is most unusual in an American clock.

Movement of the John Nicholl clock. Here, as in the John Parke clock and the Stephen Tichenor clock, is a centralization of the positioning of the "insides" of the movement because of the design for a sweep second hand. The expression "everything but the kitchen sink" is frequently used in colloquial speech. We here paraphrase the expression and say that in the repair of this clock everything was used *including* "the kitchen sink." Note the sink strainer that acts as the anchor point for the cable on the train side of the seat board.

pears that here Nicoll adopted the idea of attaching the dial in this manner, but made the part himself. The dial is also "moon phase" in type with the seconds chapter ring incorporated with that of the hour chapter ring to accommodate the indications of the sweep hand.

The case of this Nicholl tall clock is of mahogany and it is well made. The clock is owned by the Newark Museum.

John Nicholl also made a shelf clock. This was reported to the writer by a dealer in antiques in Newark, Mr. Scheiner of the firm of G. Scheiner and Son. Mr. Scheiner recalled that some years ago a shelf clock was sold by the firm that had the name, "John Nicholl, Belvidere" on the dial. Other details in the recollection of Mr. Scheiner were that the case was of mahogany with a broken arch pediment, and had brass ball and spike finials. The dimensions of the case, as Mr. Scheiner remembered are approximately 28 inches high, 16 inches wide and 5 inches deep. In Mr. Scheiner's apparently excellent memory was the fact that his firm had acquired the clock from the "Cubbage family in Belvidere" and was sold to an individual in the Haledon section of Paterson.

OGDEN, MOSES, *Newark*. Born 1736 (son of Uzal). Died July 1, 1814. Married to Mary Johnson of Elizabeth Town, June 10, 1759. Clock owned by Robert H. Hill in Ohio. Inscribed "Moses Ogden, New Ark." In the publication *Official Descriptive Catalogue of Colonial and Revolutionary Relics Now in Possession of Citizens of New Jersey* is mentioned "Clock made by Moses Ogden, 150 years old."

OSBORNE, THOMAS, and OSBORNE & WILSON, *Birmingham* (England). Names found in New Jersey clocks (and on other American clocks as well) on the calendar wheel of the painted iron dial assembly and on the "false" or "intermediate" plate. This is the iron plate mounted on the movement upon which, in turn, is mounted the dial.

Osborne & Wilson advertised in *Airis's Birmingham Gasette*, September 28, 1772 as manufacturers of clock dial plates at 3 Coleman Row. The partnership was dissolved on September 29, 1777, the same year that Thomas Osborne died.

OSTROM, C., *Newark*. Patent No. 213,999, 1879, Clock.

OWNE (EDWARD). Name found cast into the false or intermediate plate of a Morgan Hollinshead clock. According to E. J. Tyler, Hon. Curator and Librarian of the Antiquarian Horological Society of England, "Edward Owen is listed as a clock and dial maker, 3 Weaman Row, Birmingham, 1816.

Typical marking on the false or intermediate plate found on many American clocks. Similar markings are found stamped on the toothed calendar wheel. Where these markings are found, there is certainty that the dial and its component parts were imported from England. Many unmarked dials, particularly the painted iron dials, were also imported and used on the clocks of New England, Pennsylvania, and New Jersey, as well as on others. Courtesy of Ginsburg and Levy, Inc., New York.

PARKE, JOHN, *Paterson*. Late 1700's to early 1800's. On April 4, 1798, in a codicil to the will of John Stout of South Amboy, was found reference to a note for 40 pounds against John Parke, husband of Charity (daughter of John Stout), to be charged against her legacy from her father. Another date, to orient John Parke's existence as to time, is June 28, 1815, when John Parke inventoried the will of Isaac Clason "at the town of Paterson, N. J. at the Cotton Factory in the Parrot."

Two clocks are known and both are in excellent cases. The one owned by Dr. Robert Burns has a conventional type movement. The clock owned by Nelson Argueso of White Plains, New York varies in its design for a sweep seconds hand.

PARRY, JOHN, *Trenton*. 1788–1814. Harry J. Podmore, in his article "Trenton Clockmakers" (*Antiques* magazine, May 1933) wrote, "John Parry was a Philadelphia clockmaker who temporarily removed his business to Trenton in 1799 during the prevalence of yellow fever in his home city."

PARSELL, NICHOLAS, Cabinetmaker, *New Brunswick*. Son of Oliver. Born 1797. Miss Margaret White wrote, "A tall clock with a case attributed to Nicholas Parsell is owned by Catherine Schneeweiss."

PARSELL, OLIVER, Cabinetmaker, *New Brunswick*, about 1803. Label was found in a Joakim Hill clock (see illustration). Parsell was born October 4, 1757 in Ravenswood, Long Island. He worked in New York City about 1797, then moved to a farm in Neshanic, New Jersey (near Flemington and Joakim Hill). Parsell had a shop on Church Street in New Brunswick. He died in New Brunswick in 1818. His beautifully proportioned and richly inlaid clock cases show the work of a skilled and conscientious craftsman.

PATERSON, William, *Salem*. About 1848. Advertised in the *Salem Sunbeam*. Was in partnership with Bacon Ware.

PEARSON & HOLLINSHEAD, *Burlington*. 1740–1749. Isaac Pearson was the teacher of Joseph Hollinshead in the craft of clockmaking. Shortly after Joseph married Isaac's daughter Sarah they became partners.

PEARSON, ISAAC, *Burlington*. Born 1685. Died 1749. Will proved February 14, 1749, devised to, "Son-in-law Joseph Hollinshead all my Clock, Watch and Silversmiths Tools." Isaac Pearson was New Jersey's first clockmaker. Though others have been reported prior

Clock of John Parke of Paterson. Owned
by Nelson Argueso of White Plains, New
York.

Dial of the John Parke clock. The sweep second hand, provided
for in the design of the clock, is missing. The dial itself was one
to be used with a conventional second hand, as the presence of
the chapter ring for seconds indicates. The aperture in the dial for
the conventional second hand is plugged.

Movement of the John Parke clock. Note the lowering of the
bridge that is normally near the upper edge of the back plate. This
is to accommodate the rear pivot of the verge, itself lowered, as is
the rest of the mechanism to effect a sweep second design.

Clock of Isaac Pearson of Burlington of
the vintage of about 1710 to 1749. Although claims are made that other clockmakers preceded Pearson in America, no
clocks are evident. It can be then rightly
said that the owner of an Isaac Pearson
clock possesses the earliest *known* clock in
America. Photograph presented through
the courtesy of the Henry Francis du
Pont Winterthur Museum.

Hood and dial of an Isaac Pearson clock. The square dial is indicative of Pearson's earlier clocks. The lunette was not common until after about 1750. Courtesy of Ginsburg and Levy, Inc., New York.

to his date of making, 1710, there is no evidence of their work. The owner of a Pearson clock can therefore say that theirs is the oldest known clock of American make.* Of five clocks known, three are the square dial, one flat top case type and two have the lunette above the dial proper with the arched door in the hood of the case to permit its being seen.

Pearson was a worker in metals in his early life. He fashioned silver, made clocks, and was the proprietor of an iron works in Mount Holly. As early as 1738, he indicated his later bent and became elected to the General Assembly to represent the city of Burlington. Benjamin Franklin noted, in his *Autobiography* that he met Isaac Pearson. Another public office held by Pearson was that of Essay Master for Weights and Measures and Standard and Balance Keeper for the Western Division of the Province of New Jersey.

Pearson's position in the society of the day is indicated by his having indentured and/or bonded servants. Charles J. Burton, in his article about Pearson (*Bulletin of the National Association of Watch and Clock Collectors*, August 1958) mentioned a letter found on a Pearson clock written by a William Morley, who came or was brought to America in 1726, "I was sold for eleven pounds to Mr. Isaac Pearson, a man of Humanity, by trade a silversmith, clockmaker and goldsmith, living in Burlington in New Jersey. He was a Quaker, but a wet one."

Another, in Pearson's service was an Aaron Middleton, who apparently believed his fortune lay elsewhere, for on November 2, 1732 the *American Weekly Mercury* carried the advertisement of Pearson, "Run away from Isaac Pearson of the Town of Burlington, the 4th of this Instant November, a Servant man named Aaron Middleton, a Clockmaker by Trade..."

In his will, Isaac Pearson left his clockmaking tools to his son-in-law, Joseph Hollinshead, and his silversmithing tools to another son-in-law, Thomas Rodman. Pearson was buried in the Quaker cemetery in Burlington.

----

*Two other clockmakers have been reported as being in America before Isaac Pearson: Jesse E. Coleman, in his article, "Early American Clocks and Their Makers," written in the magazine *Horology*, April 1936, mentioned an "Everardus Bogardus in New York City in 1698." Coleman did not mention any known clock by Bogardus. In the same article was mentioned a "William Davis." Of him, Coleman wrote only that he "came from England and landed in Boston in 1683. Davis is not listed as a member of The London Clockmakers Company." Again no clock of Davis' make is mentioned. Since it is known that Pearson was born in 1685 and young men were in those days at a productive stage at their trade at the age of eighteen or twenty, the writer deduces that Isaac Pearson was making clocks at the age of twenty or twenty-five years of age. Hence the estimate that Pearson's clocks were made beginning in 1710 and perhaps as early as 1705.

Example of an Isaac Pearson clock having a dial with the arching lunette and its accompanying curved door in the hood. Reproduced from *Silversmiths of New Jersey* by Carl Williams through the courtesy of George S. MacManus Company, Philadelphia.

An Isaac Pearson clock having a lunette design of dial. From an article by Charles J. Burton in the *Bulletin* of the National Association of Watch and Clock Collectors.

PLUMB, D. S., *Newark.* Listed in *Newark City Directory* 1905–1926, "Manufacturer of Clock Work."

PLUMB AND MARCUS, *Newark.* 1882. 289 Washington Street. Listed in *Industries of New Jersey, Essex County* as "Plumb and Marcus, Manufacturers of Fine Clocks."

PRENTISS, HENRY S., Born July 6, 1859, *Vevey, Switzerland.* Died May 4, 1907 Elizabeth, New Jersey. Henry S. Prentiss was born in Switzerland because his American parents were en route in their travels in Europe at the time. Illness in the family detained them for two years before they returned to their native city of New York, where his father, Reverend George L. Prentiss, was a minister.

Prentiss attended a private school in New York City before leaving for New Jersey where he was to spend most of his life. Upon graduating from Princeton University in 1882 he enrolled at Stevens Institute of Technology where he acquired the degree Mechanical Engineer in 1884.

Upon leaving college Prentiss worked for a short time for the Ferracute Company in Bridgeton, New Jersey (from 1884 to 1885) and then left to work for the Hammond Typewriter Company in New York (from 1885 to 1887).

In 1889 Henry S. Prentiss married Eliza Roberts of Elizabeth, New Jersey. They established residence at 1264 Waverly Place in Elizabeth and lived at that address until his death in 1907. He is buried in Evergreen Cemetery in that city. He was active in the affairs of the Westminster Presbyterian church and served as an Elder. His importance as a citizen of Elizabeth was implied by the fact that his obituary was literally "front page news" and appeared there in the *Elizabeth Daily Journal* on May 4, 1907.

The accompanying table of Henry S. Prentiss' 28 patents will indicate the extent of his efforts in the world of horology.

The calendar clocks of Henry S. Prentiss have been variously identified as such. In the advertisement shown here the name "The Prentiss Clock Improvement Co." may be noted. On the dial of a calendar clock owned by Harry Bittner of Florham Park, New Jersey is inscribed simply "Prentiss New York" with Prentiss' patent date of Dec. 10th, 1899 on the movement. The name Lockwood & Almquist Incorporated, New York appears on the dials of several others known. One of these, owned by the author, has also the patent date Dec. 10, 1889 on the clock movement, and the patent dates April 5, 1887 and May 20, 1890 on the calendar movement. Also on the case just behind the "trap" door at the bottom is stamped, "Property of Prentiss

Calendar and Time Co. New York." This latter implies that Prentiss may have leased his calendar clocks as well as sold them.

In regard to the names Lockwood & Almquist on the dial of some of the Prentiss clocks, Miss C. R. Prentiss, a daughter of Henry S. Prentiss (whom it was the author's good fortune to find) said "Mr. Lockwood was one of the men who (along with Almquist and George L. Prentiss, a brother of Henry S. who was one of the executors of his estate) tried to keep the business going after Father died. They failed." Miss Prentiss had no knowledge of Almquist, but assumed that he was a "businessman like Lockwood."

In the *City Directory* of Elizabeth, New Jersey for 1889 through 1907, the first mention of a business address was in 1897, this at 49 Dey

Year	Invention	Number
1887	Calendar clock	360725
1889	Clock mvt. and the like	416804
''	Electric cam	417742
1890	Calendar	428318
''	Multiple cam	428319
''	Calendar	441443
1891	Clock case	450528
''	Supplemental pendulum bob	450529
''	Clock case	450530
''	Electric transmitting clock	452955
''	Synchronizer for electric clocks	452956
''	Calendar	458490
1892	Display device	477382
''	Automatic keyboard operator	487936
1893	Electric synchronizer for clocks	496134
''	''	496135
''	''	502381
''	''	506936
1894	''	517480
1895	''	533919
''	''	547358
1896	Detachable spout for cand (one-half interest)	571852
''	Self winding clock	572274
1899	Time-switch	632145
1905	Clock-movement	794380
1908	Electric signalling clock	879410
''	Self winding clock	879411
1910	Watchman's time detector	973383

Patents Issued to Henry S. Prentiss, of New York, N.Y. and Elizabeth, New Jersey. (Compiled by Larry L. Vanice, NAWCC, No. 6363, Fort Wayne, Indiana).

A Prentiss calendar clock owned by the author. The case is of two parts. The back, to which the clock movement is attached, and the deep front which covers all and is slid off and on in a manner similar to the hood of a tall clock. Note the "trap" door at the bottom (left down for demonstration purposes in the photograph). When this door is opened, the adjusting nut of the pendulum is accessible.

The two movements, calendar and clock, of the Prentiss clock. The clock movement is his "Pat. Dec. 10th 1889." On the lower right plate of the calendar movement is stamped, "Pat's. April 5th 1887 May 20th 1890 Model No. 217," and also the number "2180." In operation, the lever extending to the left over the days-of-the-week drum is pushed downward at midnight each day by the rod just above it. The calendar movement compensates itself for the odd days of the month *and* for leap year.

Street, New York. It is evident that Prentiss had a previous factory in New York. We quote from Prentiss family records, part of a letter written by a grandfather of Miss C. R. Prentiss and dated 18 April, 1891 (note that this is seven years before the first mention in the 1889 *Elizabeth Directory*), "You saw perhaps an account of the bad fire on the West Side and the burning of Henry's clock and calendar establishment. The destruction was very bad and it is a serious misfortune. A thousand finished clocks all gone and some 70 men thrown out of employment." We may judge that this establishment was of some magnitude.

Advertisement in 1903 of The Prentiss Clock Improvement Co.

Interest in the Prentiss calendar clocks is evidenced by questions asked and some information offered in the *Bulletin* of the National Association of Watch and Clock Collectors (April, 1958, August, 1963; October, 1963). A letter in the April 1958 issue, sent by J. P. M. Haas of Baltimore, Maryland, contained interesting and informative knowledge of the Prentiss calendar clock derived from his experiences with one he owned. Mr. Haas wrote "I happened to remember the booklet of instructions stated that it automatically took care of leap years. At this point I was working the month of January so when February turned I wondered what would happen. Lady Luck was certainly with me for the dates ran to 29, and then went to the 1st of March and 1956 was leap year. I continued to manually operate (the calendar mechanism) until October or November correct date and it has been running ever since, February 1957 registering 28 days and March 1st followed. It, to me, is a wonderful piece of mechanical ingenuity. All that is necessary is to keep it wound. The 30 and 31 day months are automatically taken care of. One winding is good for any month."

In winding *his own* Prentiss calendar clock the author has changed from a key to a crank (it takes 192 turnings of a key to fully wind the clock). The use of a crank is possible because, in the design of the clock the two powerful mainsprings that keep it running for a whole month are wound simultaneously from a central "winding wheel."

There is therefore but a single winding arbor. Apart from those clocks which are wound directly and where there is a kickback each time the key is turned, the intermediate winding wheel results in a smoother, easier winding, almost as in winding a weight-driven clock. This design in winding, of an intermediate winding wheel is found also in the Waltham auto clock and travel clock mechanism.

The activities of Henry S. Prentiss other than his inventions and his manufacture of calendar clocks are relatively obscure. That they were many and varied, and almost all related to timekeeping and time-keepers, can be learned from the number and nature of the 28 patents granted to him.

In speaking with Miss C. R. Prentiss, she recalled that her father "installed the time and signalling system in School No. 1, in Elizabeth, about 1900." Also, "he sent workmen to Elizabeth from New York to repair the tower clock, when the steeple was toppled from the First Presbyterian church by a tornado."

Should justification be required to include the name of Henry S. Prentiss in a listing of New Jersey names of clockmakers the author believes it right to do so based on Prentiss' having spent 25 of his 48 years in this state. He attended Princeton University and Stevens Institute for six years, worked in Bridgeton for one year, married an Elizabeth, New Jersey lady and lived the rest of his life in that city. Though his business was *in* New York, surely it can be said he was *of* New Jersey.

PRESSAQ, JOHN. Advertised as a "Watchmaker and Watch Repairer" in the New Jersey Advocate and Advertiser of Middlesex and Essex Countys (*sic*), Tuesday, October 9, 1827.

PRICE, ROBERT Jr., *Elizabeth Town*. About 1810. Price operated a brass foundry on East Jersey Street where he made andirons, shovels, tongs, machinery parts, and clock works.

PROBASCO, JACOB, *Lambertville*. Born 1802. Listed in *Kirkbride's Directory* 1850–51.

PROBASCO, JOHN, *Trenton*. 1800–1823. No clocks of Probasco's are known. Podmore mentions in his book *Trenton—Old and New* that John Huston was employed by Probasco in his store near the northeast corner of Warren and State Streets. In 1820 Probasco was given charge of the town clock originally installed by John Huston. Probasco moved to Lebanon, Ohio where he advertised in 1823 as a

"Watch and Clock Maker formerly of Trenton, New Jersey." The date of Probasco's arrival in Ohio was confirmed by J. S. Henderson.

PRUSEN, RUDOLPH, *Trenton.* Listed in *Kirkbride's Directory* 1850–51, "Clock and Watch Maker at 45 East State Street."

RADIO ELECTRIC CLOCK CORPORATION, *Elizabeth,* 1929. Listed under "Clock Mfrs." in *Elizabeth City Directory.*

REA, GEORGE, *Flemington* and *Princeton.* Born 1774 in Pittstown. Died 1838. Buried in the Baptist churchyard in Flemington. Worked in Trenton and Princeton. Two clocks dated, one 1796 and another 1797. One owned by Mr. and Mrs. Aaron Johnson (see photograph) has inscribed "George Rea Princeton" on the dial. The viewer will probably do what is called in theatrical circles, "a double take" on seeing the most unusual completed arch on the hood of the case. On close study the writer found no reason to believe that this is not original, in every sense of the word. The eye is so accustomed to seeing a broken arch on clock cases and other cabinet work, that seeing such a completed one is somewhat startling. All of the case shows the tool marks of hand crafting. The dial appears English as is the false plate into which is cast the name "Wilson." The movement has characteristics of being American made.

    The Rea clock with the 1797 date on the dial was not seen by the writer. It was seen, and reported by Mr. Ed. Davis as being 7 feet 4 inches tall with an arched door. The case of walnut with an unusual curly maple door in the body of the case. The hood is flat topped.

REED, ISAAC, *New Brunswick.* Advertised in the *New Brunswick Advertiser,* March 27, 1798. See Wheeler, Charles.

REED, SILAS G., *New Brunswick.* 1812–1814.

REEVE(S), BENJAMIN, *Greenwich.* Born 1737. Died 1801. Clocks inscribed "Benj. Reeve, Greenwich." Reeve was apprenticed to Thomas Stretch in Philadelphia and was in business for himself there. An advertisement of his in the *Pennsylvania Chronicle,* February 25, 1768 announced that he was living in Greenwich, Cumberland County, West New Jersey.

RIDGEWAY, JAMES Jr., *Newark.* Notice in the *Sentinel of Freedom* in 1802 stated that "he has commenced business in a shop opposite Mr. Giffords Tavern."

Clock of George Rea of Princeton. The unbroken arch in the pediment is a most unusual feature in the cabinet work. The author examined this with particular care and determined that the wood and the work are original and handcrafted. The maker of the case is unknown, but the workmanship is of superior quality. Owned by Aaron Johnson of Pluckemin.

Dial and hood of the George Rea clock.

ROBERTS, S. & E., *Trenton.* Listed in *Kirkbride's Directory* 1850–51, "Clock and Watch Makers at 81 Warren Street."

ROBERTS, SILAS (SAMUEL?), *Trenton.* 1790–1820.

RODMAN, ISAAC PEARSON, *Burlington.*

RODMAN, JOHN, *Burlington.* Died 1756.

ROSETT, ABRAHAM, *Elizabeth Town.* Advertised 1804–1808. Advertisement noted in the *Jersey Journal* for March 24, 1807 and several times in the weeks thereafter. It was headed by an elaborate cut depicting a cradle, an arched or bowed piece not recognizable to the writer, and a coffin. It read, "The Subscriber having taken into partnership Abraham Marsh Mulford, the Cabinet Making Business, formerly conducted by him, will in the future, be carried out under the firm of, Rosett & Mulford. Abraham Rosett." The partnership dissolved in 1808, but the business was continued by Rosett until

Advertisement of Abraham Rosett. Courtesy of Rutgers University Library of Special Collections.

his death in 1815, "Near the stone bridge in Elizabeth Town." A clock case ascribed to Rosett & Mulford was illustrated in *Antiques* magazine March 1931 on page 323. A label was also seen in the case for an Isaac Brokaw clock. The spelling of Rosett, used herein, is that found in the above advertisement, the spelling Rossett and Rousett has been seen elsewhere.

ROSETT & MULFORD, *Elizabeth Town*. See Rosett, Abraham.

ROWAND, JAMES, *Princeton*. Listed in *Kirkbride's Directory* 1850–1851.

RYERSON, LUCAS, *Paterson* and *Pompton*. Born November 26, 1771. Died March 18, 1855. Though known as a silversmith of Paterson, the location of Pompton on the dial of one of his clocks shows him to have been located there also. In the *Ryerson Genealogy* (published privately in Chicago in 1916) Lucas is mentioned as a maker of tall clocks. Other clocks known as owned by Dr. Ryerson in Boonton and one owned by Mrs. Albert Woodruff in Brooklyn, N.Y. Thanks to Mrs Samuel Schwartz for the genealogical information and alerting the writer to his existence as a clockmaker.

SAYRE, ELIAS, *Elizabeth Town* and *Middletown*. Late 1700's and early 1800's. Clock in Marlpit Hall, Middletown dial inscribed, "Elias Sayre, Monmouth," with a case by Ichabod Williams. From the Sayre Family Genealogy by Theodore M. Banta, "Elias Sayre, born in Elizabeth, New Jersey, married Jane Hetfield..." "He was a clockmaker in Elizabeth and died prior to April 12, 1815, the date of his widow's death.

SCHMID, J., *New Brunswick*. Patent No. 293,096, 1884, for Music Box Attachment for Clocks.

SCHOONMAKER, HENRY, *Paterson* or *Passaic*. Clock mentioned by Margaret White with dial inscribed, "Henry Schoonmaker, Pollifly, N.J.' Pollifly was a neighborhood region of Hackensack. There is still a Pollifly Road between Hasbrouck Heights and Hackensack. Henry Schoonmaker was born January 2, 1804 and christened in Passaic. He lived for a time on Terrace Avenue in Hasbrouck Heights, he died on June 8, 1876 and is buried in the New York cemetery in Hackensack. A clock otherwise unidentified but ascribed to Henry Schoonmaker in its records is in the First Dutch Reformed Church in Hackensack. The paper in the clock reads as follows, "This clock was made by Henry Schoonmaker of Paterson, New Jersey. It

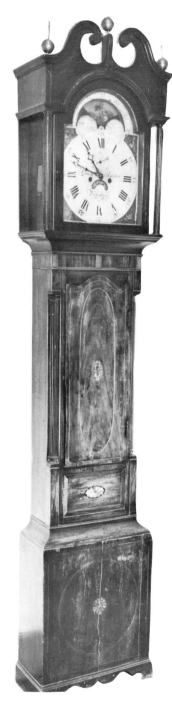

Clock by Lucas Ryerson. In his work as a silversmith, Ryerson was known to be located in Paterson. The Pompton location shown on the dial was not found elsewhere in reference to Ryerson.

Dial of the Lucas Ryerson clock.

Clock of Henry Schoonmaker. Owned by
First Reformed Church, Hackensack.

was inherited by Abram A. G. Demarest and for many years stood in the home of him and his wife Rachel Demarest in Hackensack, N.J. It was handed down to their daughter, Mary Demarest Smith of Oradell, N.J. and to their daughter Margarite Helena Smith, who in June 1960 presented it to the First Reformed church of Hackensack, N.J.''

SCHOONMAKER, ISAAC, *Paterson*. Early 1800's. Clock in Montclair. Two clocks owned by Robert L. Myers of York, Pa. One of these has writing under the saddle board, "Isaac Schoonmaker, Maker, October 11, 1811." Another, owned by Oscar Appel, has written on the inside of the case door, "Made in the year 1822 for Garret (J–I or L) Brinkerhoff."

SCHUMO, THOMAS, *Woodbury*. 1837. Listed in *Kirkbride's Directory* of 1850–1851 as clock and watchmaker of Gloucester County. In Frank H. Stewart's *Notes on Old Gloucester County* mention is made that "Thomas Schumo advertised that he would return at his old stand, next door to the surrogate's office, and resume the clock business with its allied Branches." This in 1837.

SCUDDER, JOHN, *Elizabeth Town*. Born in Westfield 1773. Moved to Ohio 1815. Cabinetmaker, made clock cases for Joakim Hill and the Brokaws.

The American line of the Scudder family began with Thomas who emigrated from London. In 1653 he was living in Salem, Massachusetts. John Scudder, a son of Thomas, moved from Salem to Long Island and from there the family moved to New Jersey. The name John persisted in the family and "our" cabinetmaker was thusly born in Westfield in 1773. His age and location would make it appear that he was not the John Scudder in the annals of the Revolutionary War who attained the rank of captain in the army. Scudder's cabinet work, judging by the quality of the clock cases he made (see photograph) was excellent. He was known to burn his initials into the wood of his cabinetry and sometimes used "Jr." after his name.

Known altogether as a cabinetmaker, his name is found on the dial of one clock known. Although this does not make the man a clockmaker, the writer reports herewith what was found. The owner of this clock, Robert L. Myers, a sophisticated collector of clocks, noted on the back of a picture he took and sent the writer, "John Scudder 1767–1846. This name is doubtful." How and why this name should appear on the dial is not too difficult to deduce. Many, perhaps most, ordinary owners of a clock think largely if not altogether of it as a

Clock of Isaac Schoonmaker of Paterson. Owned by Mr. and Mrs. George Y. Hughes of Montclair.

Dial and hood of the Isaac Schoonmaker
clock.

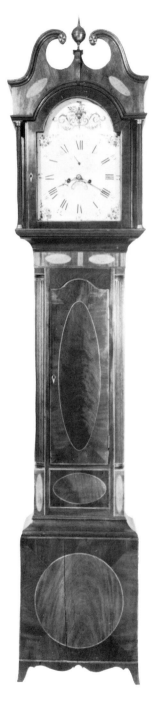

Splendid example of the fine cabinet work of John Scudder of Elizabeth Town. Its quiet grace and style, although dominant, is not domineering. Here is a reversal of the usual situation where the casemaker is known, but the clockmaker is not. Owned by Mr. and Mrs. Frederick Frelinghuysen of Holmdel. Photograph is through the courtesy of Israel Sack, Inc., New York.

Label, or what is left of it, in the case made by John Scudder.

piece of furniture. It is probable then, that some time, for whatever reason, a previous owner believing the case to have been made by John Scudder (as well it might) ergo, they have a "John Scudder clock." At some time, the paint on the dial became chipped or was peeling, making the name on the dial illegible. What name should be put on the dial in refinishing it? "Why," the owner would say, "John Scudder of course." The writer has heard curators and museum directors speak of their "Egerton clock" or "We think it's a "Scudder clock."

SHOEMAKER, DAVID, *Mount Holly*. Middle and late 1700's. De Cou, in his book *The Historic Rancocas*, has a picture of a Shoemaker clock as a frontispiece. He relates that Shoemaker was "a maker of tall clocks in Mount Holly about 1785." David Shoemaker was one of the New Jersey clockmakers who numbered his clocks. One in Haddonfield environs was found to be in the 150's, the last number was undecipherable. The inscription on the dial was "D. Shoemaker, Mount Holly." The dial was moon phase, the case of cherry and well made.

SHOURDS, SAMUEL, *Bordentown*. Drepperd, Palmer, and White agree roughly on the years, 1740–58–60 that Shourds was at work. We could find no date but one, that of his marriage to "Elizabeth" on June 11, 1759. One clock is in Morristown and one in Bordentown. The Bordentown clock is inscribed, "Samuel Shourds Bordentown Fecit."

SOMERS, ALBERTUS, *Woodbury* and *Woodstown*. Was apprenticed to George Hollinshead, taking over his shop in 1820. Moved to Woodbury in 1821, advertising in the *Village Herald* that he was taking over the business of John Whitehead, who had moved to Haddonfield. A clock in Wilmington, Delaware of Albertus Somers is owned by Mr. and Mrs. Gerald D. Montaigne, direct descendants of the original owners. Family records state that it was made for Samuel Dickeson and his wife (Sarah Pancost). The clock was made while Somers was at Elderidges Hill near Woodstown, Salem County.

SPEAR, THOMAS Jr., *Bloomfield*. Advertised in the "*Sentinel of Freedom*" February 10, 1817 as "Opposite the Academy."

SPEER, A. S., *Passaic*. Patent No. 347,528, 1886 for Illuminated Clock, Hands, and Dial. Patent No. 407,945, 1889 for Electric Clock for Exposed Places.

STILES, MOSES, *Rahway*. Born in Morristown April 2, 1771. Stiles was a farmer and clockmaker. He died at Morris Plains, August 22, 1854. This clock, see figure, now owned by Edward J. Grassmann of Elizabeth, was formerly owned by Roy Vail of Warwick, New York. The name of Moses Stiles is inscribed within the painted shell in the lunette of the dial. Mr. Vail's discerning eye discovered six different kinds of wood from which the case was fashioned.* Cherry, curly maple, walnut, holly, ebony plus mahogany veneer. If we add to this the probable pine back and gluing blocks, this makes an unusual array of wood with which to make a case. The case maker is unknown.

STILLMAN, JOSEPH, *New Germantown*. Clock, see figure. Although the dial and its false plate are obviously the kind imported from England, the unusual hands and the movement of the clock appear to have been made here. An oddity in the movement is that this is the only movement seen, other than Aaron Miller's and the Brokaw's, where a piece of one of the plates has been cut out. On all others it

---

*An almost identical instance was found by the writer, some years ago, in a case that had been made for Simon Willard.

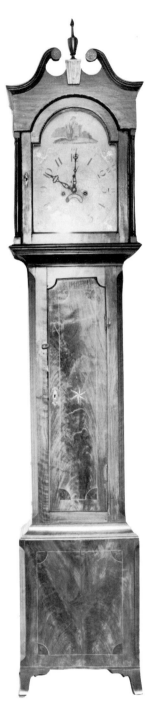

Clock by Albertus Somers. Owned by a
direct descendent of the original owner,
Mr. and Mrs. Gerald D. Montaigne of
Wilmington, Delaware.

Clock by Moses Stiles of Rahway. Courtesy of Roy Vail of Warwick, New York.

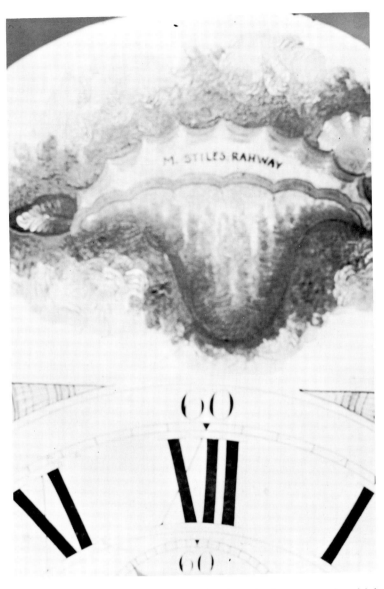

Dial of Moses Stiles clock. A variation here is the manner in which the maker affixed his name, inscribed within the ornamental painting in the lunette.

Front of the movement of the Moses Stiles clock. Although the
overall design, with the rack and snail strike and other typical
features, follows that of English clocks, hand crafting is observed
throughout. There are many details that mark this clock as the
work of an individualist—the pitted roughness of the case plates,
the slightly different design of the rack, even the tension spring
that detains the "wind vane" has a quality in design indigenous to
the maker.

224

Rear of the Moses Stiles clock movement. Here, too, are seen qualities that are individualistic—the arbors of the main wheels protrude to an unusual extent through the rear plate. Note also the cutting out of the rear plate. Did Stiles, a contemporary of the Brokaws and living in their vicinity, learn from them that if you needed a small piece of brass (hard to come by in those days), cut it out of the edge of the rear plate!

Clock of Joseph Stillman.

was found missing always from the back plate and usually off the upper right hand corner, on this clock there is a piece missing out of the upper left side of the front plate!

STREET, ZADOC, *Mannington.* The following was found in the Salem County Historical Society, in *"Relic of ye Olden Days in Salem County, New Jersey, U. S. A."* by Ann Hunter Van Meter. "Eightday clock, bought by Aaron Fogg Sen, about 1800 of Zadoc Street, a clockmaker who lived on a farm in Mannington, Salem County."

TAPPEN, JOHN, *Flemington.* About 1840, was a carpenter, cabinet-maker, and coffin maker. Made cases for Joakim Hill.

TAZEWELL, SALVO, *Bridgeton.* 1865. Clock was on exhibition at the Old Barracks in Trenton.

TICHENOR, STEPHEN, *Newark.* 1760. Clock owned by the New Jersey Historical Society in Newark. See figure. In a particularly fine curly maple case, the movement has a most unusual striking arrangement that has every evidence of being original. The striking hammer found mounted on an arbor between the plates is mounted at the rear of the back plate and strikes a gong, not a bell, that is in turn mounted on the back board of the case. Note the count wheel is the same as that of Aaron Miller and of Isaac Brokaw.

TREAT, GEORGE, *Newark.* Mentioned in the *Newark Directory,* 1850–1858. *Kirkbride's Directory* 1850–1851 listed him as of Morristown.

TRENCHARD, R., *Salem.* Clock owned by Karl A. Dickinson of Cape May. He describes it as being in a cherry wood case and having an all-brass dial engraved with floral designs. The inscription "R. Trenchard, Salem" is across the bottom of the dial.

TRENCHARD, THOMAS, *Salem.* A letter to Miss Josephine Jaquett, Librarian of the Salem County Historical Society, inquiring of possible genealogical data on R. Trenchard brought back a reply that no information was available. Miss Jaquett then revealed that in a little book in the library at the Salem County Historical Society, *Relics of Ye Olden Days* was mentioned, "Tall clock, 1734, made by Thos. Trenchard, 1st clockmaker of Salem, N.J." The clock was owned by William H. Lawson of Salem. This family has now died out or moved away.

Research has failed to reveal more about R. Trenchard or Thos.

Dial of the Joseph Stillman clock.

Stephen Tichenor clock in an exceptionally fine curly maple case. The case
maker is not known. Courtesy of the
New Jersey Historical Society, Newark.

Movement of the Stephen Tichenor clock. Noteworthy is the
design of the striking mechanism. A gong is mounted on the back-
board of the case, instead of the usual bell above the movement.
The whole appears original, not a repairman's replacement.

Trenchard (the name is found to have been variously spelled Tranchard and Trancherd) so as to reveal the probable relationship between the two clockmakers.

TRIBE, GEORGE, *Newark*. Listed in the *Newark City Directory* of the 1850's, "Clockmaker at 123 Sheffield and 119 Broome Street."

VAN BUREN, WILLIAM, *Newark*. 1792. Advertised in *Wood's Gazette* in October of that year: "Clock and Watch Maker." His advertisement, October 25, 1792, in "*Woods Newark Gazette*" reads "Gold & Silversmith... He also carries on the Clock and Watch making business in the best manner—for which Country Produce will be taken in payment."

VOUTE, LEWIS C., *Bridgeton*. 1826. Advertisement in the March 11, 1826 issue of the *Bridgeton Observer*: "Clock and Watch Making... near Mr. Buck's Hotel."

WALLACE & TIERNAN INC., *Belleville*. A manufacturer of a variety of things. Between the years 1928 and 1932 they made clocks of several types, such as tambour, banjo, kitchen and office clocks. They were all electric of the kind that winds itself on electric impulse every 15 to 30 seconds, depending on design. Only a few thousand were made. The venture was sold to the American Timing Company in Hartford, Connecticut.

CLOCK & WATCH MAKING.

THE subscriber, grateful for past favors returns his thanks to his friends and the public for the flattering encouragement he has received, and informs them that he carries on the business as usual, in all its branches, at the old stand in Bridgeton, nearly opposite to Mr. Buck's Hotel. He hopes by particular attention to merit and receive a continuance of public favor.

Clocks repaired in the best manner: from his experience in that branch of business he confidently hopes to receive the approbation of the public.

LEWIS C. VOUTE.

. P. S. L. C. Voute, would suggest to those indebted to him the propriety of discharging the amount of their several bills, as short settlements is the grand incentive to extra exertion.

March, 11th, 1826.—62-tf.

Advertisement of Lewis C. Voute.

WARE, BACON, *Salem*. From the *History of Salem County*, "Opened shop in 1819 and advertised as "Watch Maker, Salem, New Jersey" October 21, 1835. In 1948 in partnership with William Paterson on Market Street, Salem. His son Charles R. Ware, also a watchmaker in Salem, born 1831.

Mrs. Caroline B. Baker, to whom the writer owes much for her little notes frequently containing genealogical data, commented interestingly, that, "The Wares and the Bacons did a lot of marrying— that's how he got his name."

WARE, GEORGE C., *Camden*. Not of the same family line as Bacon Ware. Advertised in *Kirkbride's Directory* 1850–51 as selling "Clocks, Watches, Spectacles, Violin Strings, Musical Instruments and Jewelry."

WHEELER, CHARLES, *New Brunswick*. 1798. The following advertisement was found in the *"Guardian or New Brunswick Advertiser."*

CHARLES WHEELER & ISAAC REED
Clock and Watch Makers

Inform the public in general, that they have commenced business at the house formerly occupied by Silas Howell, where clocks of every description are made and watches repaired in the best manner—those who favour them with their custom, may depend on being well served and on the most reasonable terms; they have on hand a small assortment of chains, seals, keys and other articles in their line of business. New Brunswick, March 3, 1798.

WHITEFIELD, JOHN, *Haddonfield*. 1791–1875. This name mentioned in *The Story of New Jersey* Vol. II, p 378. The writer believes this to be a confusion with John Whitehead.

WHITEHEAD, JOHN, *Woodbury* and *Haddonfield*. Born 1791. Died 1875. Took over the shop of Job Hollinshead in 1821. An advertisement in May of that year in the *Village Herald* in Woodbury indicated that he had been located in a shop opposite the Surrogate's office in Woodbury. He was replaced there by Albertus Somers. Carl Williams gives a very interesting account of one of John Whitehead's efforts in his *Silversmiths of New Jersey 1700–1825*. Williams wrote, "About 1830 he (Whitehead) constructed a double-faced clock for the office building of the Cumberland Nail and Iron Company in Bridgeton, New Jersey. The mechanism operates one dial on the exterior of the building and another on the wall within an office room. A paneled and

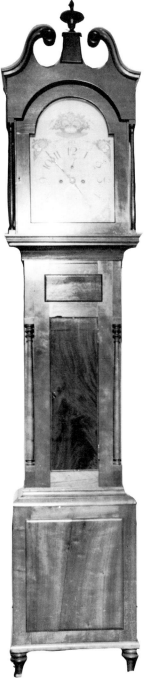

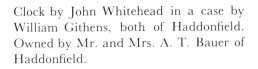

Clock by John Whitehead in a case by
William Githens, both of Haddonfield.
Owned by Mr. and Mrs. A. T. Bauer of
Haddonfield.

moulded case resembling that of a tall case clock, houses the mechanism and is built on the inside wall of the building. It is the oldest public clock in Bridgeton."

There are three clocks of Whitehead known to the writer, one in a walnut case, the dial is iron painted, no moon phase; another in a mahogany case, the dial of this one does have the moon phase feature; and the third clock known is in a cherry wood case with a mahogany door, rosettes in the scrolls and small panel over the door. The case to this third clock was made by William Githins of Haddonfield.

WILLIAMS, A. L., *Newark*. In *Newark Directory* from 1845 to 1858–59 he is listed at 7 Cedar Street, 230 Broad Street. Advertised in the *Newark Directory* for 1851–52, "Watch and Clock Maker, 226½ Broad Street. A general assortment of Jewelry, Watches, Clocks, Spoons, Spectacles &c., constantly on hand. Repairing Watches and Jewelry punctually Attended to." In spite of the label within the clock case (see figures) reading, "Made and Sold by," it would appear that Williams might have only assembled some shelf clocks. It adds to the confusion here, that the case here has two small pulley wheels in the top for the cords of a weight driven movement, while the label reads "Spring Brass Clocks." Both the pulley wheels and the label appear to be original.

The last entry in the *Newark Directory*, 1858–59, lists "Williams, Andrew L., Watch casemaker, Seneca Falls, N. Y."

Note the similarity in design between this case, with the Williams label in it and the case used by Aaron Dodd Crane for his three-ball, eight-day clock. Crane was active at this same time 1849–57 in approximately the same neighborhood.

WILLIAMS, BENJAMIN, *New Brunswick*, 1780–1791. *Trenton*, 1791–1806. Was the partner of William Leslie. *Elizabeth Town*. Advertisement 1788 "Wanted immediately as an apprentice to the Silver Smiths Business a boy of about 14 years of age, that can be well recommended. Enquire of Benjamin Williams, Elizabeth Town. April, 1788."

WILLIAMS, ICHABOD, *Elizabeth Town*. Born 1808. Cabinetmaker. Made furniture and clock cases. His label is in a case housing an Aaron Lane clock (see figure), owned by H. Kels Swan of South Bound Brook. (The same case has on its door, on the inside, the name Joakim Hill and a repair date written as usual in script with white chalk). Winterthur Museum in Wilmington, Delaware has an Ichabod Williams chair. Williams has been called variously "A farmer who did cabinet work in winter months" (White), and "Amateur

Clock case bearing the label of A. L.
Williams of Newark, evidently a jewelry
store owner. No movement was in the
case when it was found. A cause for confusion is the incompatibility of the two
pulleys in the top of the case for a weight-
driven clock, and the label stating "Eight
Day Spring Brass Clock."

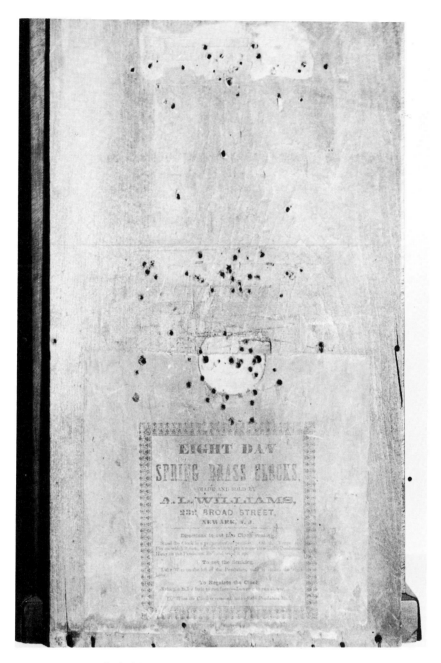

Label in the A. L. Williams clock was imprinted "Eight Day Spring Brass Clock."

Clock-Maker" (Drepperd). In the minutes of the Corporation of Elizabeth Town of May 31, 1823, Ichabod Williams was referred to as an "Engineer." In the minutes of August 21, 1824 as "Alderman." Ichabod Williams was a brother-in-law of Aaron Lane.

WILLIAMS, JOHN H., *New Brunswick*. About 1790. Had clock shop opposite the Whitehall Tavern.

WILLIAMS, THOMAS, *Flemington*. 1792–1808 in Flemington on Village Street. A clock of Williams' purported to be in the Flemington area, but not seen by the writer.

WILLIS, JOHN, *Burlington*. Before 1748. In the Calendar of Wills is stated that Willis died intestate, "John Willis, Clock Maker Intestate 10–21–1748, of the City of Burlington. Administrators: Joseph Rose, Attorney, and Charles Willis Black Smith of the same place." No clock known.

John Willis was also mentioned as a watchmaker in the will of Abraham Bryan of Burlington in 1742–43. There is mention of a John Willis marrying Elizabeth Wood on June 25, 1743.

The first Willis in America, from whom John was descended, was also a John, from Chalow, Berks County, England. He arrived before 1688.

WILSON, JAMES, *Birmingham (England)*. In partnership with Thomas Osborne making clock dials 1772–1777. Listed in 1778 as dial maker "carries on the business at 11 Great Charles Street," also listed in 1808. "St. Mary Square, Clock Dial Maker and jappaner." Died April 3, 1809 at 11 Great Charles Street (according to Birmingham Reference Library records) listed in Universal British Directory 1791 as a dial maker at this address.

This information is given through the kindness of Beresford Hutchinson of the British Museum, London, England.

WILSON, E., *Elizabeth*. Patent No. 124,104, 1872 for an Electric Clock.

WINTER, W., *Plainfield*. Patent No. 43,616, 1864, for Watchman's Clock.

WOOD & HUDSON, *Mount Holly*. About 1790–1810. Partnership of John Wood and William Hudson. A clock by Wood having a brass dial ca. 1765–1775 is reported by Edward F. La Fond, Jr., Wilmington, Dela.

WOOD, JOHN, *Mount Holly*. Born 1736. Died about 1793.

WYCOFF (See Cortelyou and Wycoff).

YATES & KENT, *Trenton*. 1798. Advertised in the *New Jersey Gazette*, "Yates and Kent, Clock and Watch Makers, Jewellers and Silversmiths. At this shop between the Indian-Queen and City Hall, Trenton, beg leave to inform their friends and the public in general, that they carry on the above business in all their branches, and have now on hand an elegant assortment of Silver and Jewelry Ware, consisting of Table and Tea Spoons, Cream Jugs, Tea Bowls, Knee and Shoe Buckles, Ear and Finger Rings; etc. etc. which they are determined to sell on the lowest terms for Cash or Old Silver in exchange. They have likewise an elegant card of devices for Lockets or Rings. All orders executed with elegance and dispatch. Clocks and Watches made and sold as usual. Trenton May 7, 1798."
Shop was taken over by Leslie and Williams in 1803.

YATES, JOSEPH, *Trenton*. About 1780–1817 are the estimated years that Yates was occupied with clocks. He was the Yates in the partnership of Yates and Kent. In 1803 he moved to Freehold, but an advertisement of his placed him back in Trenton in 1817. The advertisement was as a proprietor of a tavern.

YEAR CLOCK COMPANY, *New York City*, 1845–46. Listed in Daggett's *New York City Directory* as at "109 Fulton Street" under the name of "J. R. Mills." Other labels in clocks have the address as 35 Cortlandt Street, New York City. All of these clocks are those of Aaron Dodd Crane and all were made either in Belleville or in Newark, New Jersey. The New York City addresses are evidence only of the attempts of J. R. Mills to establish a point of sales and distribution. (See Crane, Aaron Dodd for details and names of the organizers of the Year Clock Company).
Note: Listed in the *New York City Directory* for 1903–05 was another "Year Clock Company" at 79 Crosby Street. This had no relationship with Crane's Year Clock Company.

YOUNG, JACOB, *Elizabeth Town*, 1750–1760. According to Arthur F. Cole, an historian of early Elizabeth, Young was a clockmaker in Elizabeth Town who, "Went to the Manheim section of Philadelphia later."

YUNKER, ADOLPH, *Trenton*. It was reported to the writer by Carl

238

Peters of Titusville that a clock with the above name was owned by a Charles Hazelhurst of Wyncote, Pa. The apparent removal of Mr. Hazelhurst has thwarted efforts of the writer to "follow through" up to this point. Mr. Peters said that the name was barely distinguishable and that some letters in it were missing altogether.

Inside the case of a John Guild clock was found a small piece of plain paper upon which was written in script, "Adolph Yunker, Clock Maker, No. 326 Green Str., Trenton, May 6, 1881."

Pair of typical "New England" shelf clocks. This type of clock revolutionized the clockmaking industry not only in America, but throughout the world. After their coming, clockmaking in New Jersey, with but few exceptions, ceased to exist.

Watchmaking in New Jersey

THE HISTORY of watchmaking in America was one of "Here today and gone tomorrow." The establishments to make watches in New Jersey were no exception. A thesis could be written on the whys and wherefores of the rise and downfall of watch factories and of those that died aborning, in New Jersey and throughout the country. This is not the place for such a perusal of business philosophies or the lack of sound ones. Succinctly and completely, perhaps more eloquently than fine rhetoric, the following expressions tell the story. These are expressions garnered from various sources telling of the history of watch manufacture in America:

"... name was changed."
"... name was changed again."
"... abandoned the business."
"... the company practically failed and was reorganized."
"... it failed."
"... it sold out to ..."
"... it ceased business."
"... it again failed."
"... the business was taken over by ..."
"... in turn was later purchased by ..."
"... the property and business were sold to ..."
"... it was reorganized under the same name"
"... sold its business and property to ..."
"... was organized ... it failed."
"... the business was sold to ..."
"... the company made a voluntary assignment."
"... it was reorganized under the name of ..."
"... failed the same year."
"... continued in operation about ten years."
"... began operations in 1885, failed in 1886."
"... was organized but failed after two years."
"... but did not long continue."

Ironically, the most successful company in New Jersey in the watch industry, was from Pennsylvania, the Keystone Watch Case Company of Philadelphia. In 1902 it controlled The New York Standard Watch Company of Jersey City, The Crescent Watch Case Company of Newark, and The Philadelphia Watch Case Company of Riverside, all of New Jersey. The Howard Watch Company of Waltham, Massachusetts was at this same time also controlled by the Keystone Watch Case Company.

However transitory the business of watch making was in New Jersey, as it was in the rest of the country, millions of serviceable watches were produced. Too, there were thousands of people employed over the years in their factories giving income to those employed as well as a training that, as the factories themselves disintegrated, could be well used elsewhere. Although individuals suffered by the failure of the watch factories, the state and the nation benefited by their being.

Watchmakers of New Jersey

ABBOTT, HENRY, *Newark, New York City* and *Harrison,* 1850 to 1893. Henry Abbott's family moved to Rahway in 1861, when Henry was about 11 years of age. He learned watch repairing at the age of 16 from Gaven Spence on Broad Street in Newark. At the age of 21 Abbott opened a store of his own on Maiden Lane in New York City. Abbott's inventive mind—he had more than 40 patents—brought him into the company of those similarly interested, and he and Edward Howard became friends.

Among Abbott's many patents were Stem Winding and Setting Watches, Interchangeable Watch Movement, and Applying Color to Enamel of Watch Dials. In the application of his stem winding and setting inventions, Abbott is said to have converted more than 100,000 watches from key-wind to stem-wind.

Perhaps the most remunerative were the inventions that grew into the manufacture of the Calculagraph, an internal timer used in large numbers by telephone companies for timing calls, and by many others for similar purposes. The Calculagraph Company still flourishes in New Jersey. (For more information see Calculagraph.)

AJAX WATCH INSULATOR. See Newark Watch Case Material Company.

ALEXANDER, W. Model of the United State Watch Company.

AMERICAN NATIONAL WATCH COMPANY. The charter of the American National Watch Company was filed in the office of the Department of State of the State of New Jersey on May 15, 1902. It changed its corporate name to South Bend Watch Company on June 30, 1902. The Corporation, South Bend Watch Company, was voided for nonpayment of state taxes by proclamation of the Governor on February 19, 1919 and was never reinstated.

This Ajax Insulator is an example of the many accessory products manufactured along with watches.

AMERICAN REPEATING WATCH COMPANY, *Elizabeth*, late 1800's. Located at 117 Broad Street. The company was owned and operated by F. Terstegen who advertised himself as "Inventor and Manufacturer of the American Repeating Watch; Wholesale and Retail."

How many repeating attachments were made is not known. The product, however great its sales may or may not have been, was thought well of by Henry G. Abbott. In his book, *American Watchmaker and Jeweler*, Abbott devotes a half page of text and an illustration (p 309) to favorable consideration of Terstegen's invention. Terstegen had three patents;

Patent No. 311,270, 1885, "Repeating Attachment for Watches."
Patent No. 421,844, 1890, "Repeating Mechanism for Watches or Other Timepieces."
Patent No. 436,162, 1890, "Repeating Attachment for Watches."

ATHERTON, FREDERICK W. With the Marion Watch Company, 1867.

BAKER, CALEB, *Bordentown*. Listed in *Kirkbride's Directory*, 1850–1851. Watch paper.

244

FRED. TERSTEGEN, 117 BROAD STREET,
r and M'f'r of the American Repeating Watch; Wholesale and Re

The Terstegen store in Elizabeth with several of the staff
members.

BAKER, SAMUEL, *New Brunswick*, 1822–1858. Watch paper in Rutgers University Library, Special Collections. It reads, in part, "Samuel Baker, Clock and Watch Maker, Albany Street, 1 door west of State Bank, New Brunswick," etc.

BALDWIN, S., *Newark*. Patent No. 22,397, 1858, Watch Dial.

BANISTER, G. H., *Newark*. Patent No. 218,215, 1879, Watch Case Spring.

BEARD, S. M. Model of the United States Watch Company.

BIRRN, H., *Jersey City*. Patent No. 154,636, 1874, Watch Case Back.

BLISS, E., *Newark*. Patent No. 19,966, 1858, Watch Case.

BOWEN, G. A., *Trenton*. Patent No. 73,161, 1868, Watch.

BOYNETT, E. G., *Jersey City*. Patent No. 180,521, 1876, Watch Regulator, and Patent No. 192,222, 1877, Watch.

BRIEDT, ALBERT, *Trenton*. Listed in *Kirkbride's Directory* for 1850–1851.

CHANNING, GEORGE. Model of the United States Watch Company.

COLUMBIA. Model of the New York Standard Watch Company.

CRESCENT WATCH CASE COMPANY, *Newark*, 1899. Located at 65–85 North 13th Street. Was controlled by the Keystone Watch Case Company of Philadelphia, Pennsylvania.

CROWN. Model of the New York Standard Watch Company.

DAN PATCH STOP WATCH. Model of the New York Standard Watch Company.

DEACON, J. W. Model of the United States Watch Company.

EXCELSIOR. Model of the New York Standard Watch Company.

FAYETTE STRATTON. Model of the United States Watch Company.

GILES, F. A., *Jersey City*. Patent No. 145,939, 1873, Main Spring Barrel for Watch.

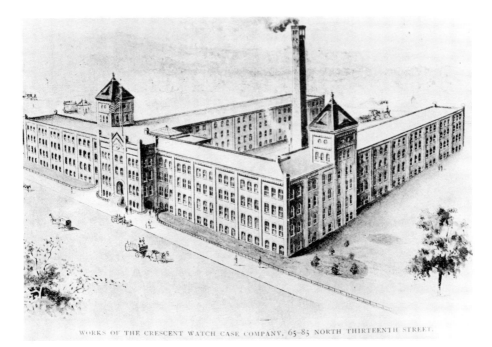

WORKS OF THE CRESCENT WATCH CASE COMPANY, 65-85 NORTH THIRTEENTH STREET.

Factory of the Crescent Watch Case Company in Newark where many thousands of watch cases were made.

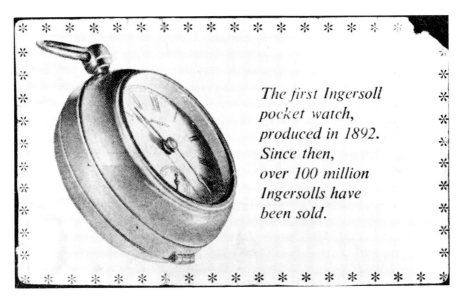

The first Ingersoll pocket watch, produced in 1892. Since then, over 100 million Ingersolls have been sold.

An early Ingersoll watch.

HIGRADE. Model of the New York Standard Watch Company.

HOLLEY WATCH COMPANY, *Jersey City*. Patents on Duplex Watch in the years 1874–78–83–84–85–86.

HORTON, W. H., *Jersey City*. Patent No. 103,190, 1870, Watch Regulator.

IDEAL. Model of the New York Standard Watch Company.

INGERSOLL, CHARLES H. Fame and fortune came to Charles Ingersoll and his older brother Robert by the manufacture of "The Watch that made the dollar famous." In New Jersey the Ingersoll factory was in Chambersburg, a suburb of Trenton. The factory had originally been that of the New Haven Watch Company, organized in 1883. Its name was changed to The Trenton Watch Company when they moved to Chambersburg in 1886. When it failed in 1907 (a nationwide depression occurred at that time) it was taken over by the Ingersoll Brothers.

In an article in the *East Orange Record* it was reported that, "At the turn of the century the Ingersoll Brothers were able to invade the European market. One firm in London started them off with an order for a million watches. Fifty million watches were to have been made by 1917."

The Ingersoll watch was so closely identified with the one dollar price that when in 1921 it was no longer possible to make the watch for that price, the company failed.

Charles Ingersoll spent most of his life in New Jersey. He was born on October 29, 1865 in Delta, Michigan. He joined his older brother Robert in New York City where at the respective ages of 15 and 20 they successfully made and sold rubber stamps. Charles took up residence in East Orange and in 1883 showed his disposition to take part in local civic (later State and National) affairs by running for City Council in the Fourth Ward of that city. He lived variously in East Orange, South Orange, Montclair, and West Orange. It was while living with his eldest daughter, Mrs. Joseph D. Sharrer, in Llewellyn Park, West Orange that, a short distance away from home, he was struck by an automobile causing injuries that resulted in his death at Orange Memorial Hospital September 21, 1948.

The greatest contribution made by the Ingersolls was the concept of universality of a product, in this case a watch (the first one was named "Universal"). To achieve this all sales, promotion, and dis-

A popular model of the Ingersoll watch.

tribution was directed to the consumer and all plans, even at the factory, were made giving the consumer primary consideration.

In the making of the "dollar watch" the Ingersolls pioneered the economic theory that increased production leads to high employment and reversed the scarcity motive in business. The value of this business philosophy was recognized and expounded by one of the country's great economists, Stuart Chase.

Having noted the beneficence of making a watch available to every man, woman, and even child, Charles H. Ingersoll tried, in later years, to apply this philosophy to other things, notably housing. In association with Thomas Edison, several houses were constructed in New Jersey that he called "the Edison-Ingersoll, $1000 concrete, six-room house."

INTERNATIONAL WATCH COMPANY. Made dollar watches in Jersey City about 1905.

JAMES, HENRY B., *Trenton*. Patent No. 107,916, Mainspring Barrel for Watch. Mentioned in *Kirkbride's Directory* for 1850 as of Mount Holly or Cahansey Township.

KEYSTONE. Model of the New York Standard Watch Company.

KEYSTONE WATCH CASE COMPANY. The Keystone Watch Case Company was organized in 1899. It at one time controlled The New York Standard Watch Company of Jersey City, The Crescent Watch Case Company of Newark and The Philadelphia Watch Case Company of Riverside, all in New Jersey. This Pennsylvania company at this time also controlled the Howard Watch Company of Waltham, Massachusetts.

KNAPP, CHARLES G. Model of the United States Watch Company.

LeFORT, H., *Newark*. Patent No. 226,329, 1880, Watch Cover, and Patent No. 372,158, 1887, Forming Pendant for Watch.

LEWIS, JOHN. Model of the United States Watch Company.

MARION WATCH COMPANY. Organized first as The United States Watch Company by Giles, Wales & Co. in 1863. It operated as such until 1872. On July 30, 1874 the Marion Watch Company was incorporated in Jersey City. It too failed. The area called Marion was absorbed into Jersey City. The factory was dismantled and the machinery was sold to Ezra Bowman of Lancaster, Pennsylvania. It was in turn sold to J. P. Stevens of Atlanta, Georgia. Other machinery was sold to the Auburndale Watch Company, Auburndale, Massachusetts; the Fredonia Watch Company, Fredonia, New York; and Fitchburg Watch Company, Fitchburg, Massachusetts. A peculiarity of the movements is the "Butterfly" shaped aperture in the watch plate under one side of the balance wheel.

MILNE, A., *Newark*. Patent 199,732, 1878, Watch Crown.

MORLET, C., *Hoboken* and *Jersey City*. Patent No. 367,995, 1887, Push Button for Repeating Watch; Patent No. 387,247, 188, Repeating Watch; and Patent No. 402,247, Balance Staff for Watch.

NEW ERA. Model of the New York Standard Watch Company.

NEWARK WATCH CASE MATERIAL COMPANY. Manufacturer of the Ajax Watch Insulator, a device made of a ferrous material claimed to shield the watch it contained against magnetic influences and was also a mechanical protection against breakage of crystals in the open face types of watches. Patented October 29, 1899.
    The company was located in Newark on the corner of Mechanic and Ward Streets in 1874. In the *Essex County, New Jersey Illustrated*,

Factory of the Newark Watch Case Material Co. where the Ajax
Watch Insulator was made.

published in 1897 it was noted that this was, an "Enterprise of Alexander Milne, the founder of the stem winding attachment now in general use in American made watches." The writer does not subscribe to the accuracy of this quotation.

NEWARK WATCH COMPANY. Organized in New York City by jewelry store owners, Messers. Fellows and Schell. After a few months, due to lack of space, the establishment was moved to Newark in 1864. The *Newark Directory* of 1865–66 listed them as "Newark Watch Manufacturing Company, 258 Market Street." Their technical "expert" in charge was the head watchmaker of their previous jewelry store, Arthur Wadsworth.

Production was delayed and in the first year of production (1867) only 400 watches were sold. This increased to 1000 in 1868 and 1500 in 1869 when the company stopped making watches. The machinery, completed watches and parts were sold in 1871 to what became the Cornell Watch Company in Chicago, Illinois. (The Cornell Watch Company moved to California in 1874).

The Newark Watch Company employed two types of dials. One was inscribed "Newark Watch Company, N.J.," the other "Newark Watch Works, N.J." All of their watches were 18S, full plate with a small plate over the mainspring barrel, English side lever escapement.

As was customary in the manufacture of watches in those days, the dials and/or movements were inscribed with the name of the dealer who was selling the watch; the name of one of the upper echelon boys or even the name of a generous investor. Names on some of the Newark Watch Company movements were Edward Biven, Henry Harrison and A. K. P. Walker, Arthur Wadsworth. Of the Wadsworth watch, H. F. Piaget wrote in his book *The Watch*, p 55, "The Keyless or Wadsworth Watches, manufactured at Newark, New Jersey. There is a watch manufactury at the above place, where a very excellent watch is made, with an improved patented winding and setting arrangement. From what I have seen of it, I should say it would not be likely to get out of order. It is very simple in its construction. The movements are full upper plates, chronometer balances, well jeweled, and very nicely finished. I approve very much the whole getting up of the watch."

NEW HAVEN WATCH COMPANY. Originally in New Haven, Connecticut in 1883. Moved to Chambersburg, New Jersey, a suburb of Trenton, in 1886. In 1887 the name was changed to the Trenton

Watches of the New Haven Watch Company such as might have been made at their Chambersburg Factory about the time they sold out to the Ingersoll Company.

New Jersey Watch Company, Mercer
Model No. 01, 855.

Rear of the Mercer Model No. 01, 855
with the cover removed.

Watch Company and failed in 1907. It was sold to Robert H. Ingersoll & Brother in 1908.

In the illustrations, the larger "watch" $2\frac{1}{2}$ inches across and $1\frac{1}{2}$ inch thick is the earliest of the dollar watches as made also by the Waterbury and Ingersoll factories. Its size probably engendered the apt descriptive terms "Turnip" and "Potato."

NEW YORK STANDARD WATCH COMPANY, *Jersey City*. Located in 1885 at 193 Woodward Street, at Communipaw Avenue. One of the more prolific manufacturers of watches in New Jersey, they made many models, some cased in solid gold. The movements were not of the highest grade, but much superior to the average watch made in the state particularly the "dollar" pin lever type. An excellent work-a-day kind of timepiece from the mechanical point of view.

A unique model made in 1887, jokingly called "The watch with a worm in it," was based on Patent No. 286685 issued to Robert J. Clay of Jersey City. The principle of this patent, on the escapement, was in the use of a contrate wheel and worm (endless screw). A later patent, No. 356187 was issued jointly to Clay and William Hanson of Brooklyn, New York altering the original patent by substituting a plain wheel and omitting the costly yoke. This model, after some 12,000 were made, was discontinued in favor of the more conventional lever escapement. As unique as the escapement on this model, was the setting arrangement.

The sources for the above "watch with a worm in it" are an article by Major Paul M. Chamberlain "Notes on the Lever Escapement," *Horology* magazine, August, 1938; an article "Unusual Setting Arrangement" by Joseph Dean in the *Watchmakers Journal* May–June, 1960. Illustrations also are from the same sources.

The company was purchased by the Keystone Watch Case Company in 1902.

PARKER, F., *Jersey City*. Patent No. 235,010, 1880, Watch Case.

PERFECTION, Model of the New York Standard Watch Company.

PHILADELPHIA WATCH CASE COMPANY, *Riverside*, 1890's. Owned by the Keystone Watch Case Company of Philadelphia, Pennsylvania.

RANDEL, HENRY. Model of the United States Watch Company.

REGENT. Model of the New York Standard Watch Company.

Unique watch design of the New York
Standard Watch Company.

Rear of the New York Standard watch
with cover removed.

Winding and setting mechanism of the New
York Standard watch. Note the large internal
gear crown wheel. The set lever is shown
pushed in and in contact with the ratchet wheel
for winding. When in the setting position, the
rocking bar setting bridge pivots on its screw.
The crown wheel disconnects from the ratchet
wheel and the setting wheel moves down to mesh
with the minute wheel.

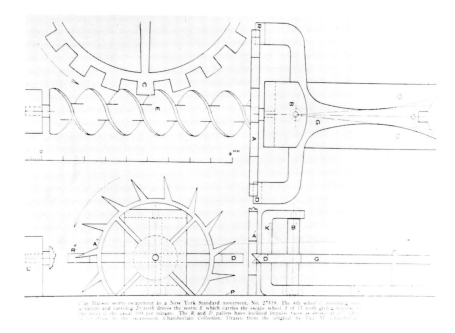

Clay-Hanson escapement as used in an early New York Standard
watch. The illustrations of the New York Standard watches are
through the courtesy of Orville R. Hagans and *Horology* magazine.

New Jersey watch factories, as did others, assumed the obligation
to supply replacement parts for their watches. This photograph is
of a packet for mainsprings as sold to ''the trade'' for replacing
weakened or broken mainsprings in New York Standard watches.

REID, G. A. Model of the United States Watch Company.

ROLLO, EDWIN. Model of the United States Watch Company.

RUTMAN, C., *Jersey City*. Patent No. 289,359, 1883, Watch Regulator.

SANDOZ, E., *Hudson Town* (now Jersey City). Patent No. 97,123, 1869, Cannon Pinion for Watch.

SCHLATTER, C., *Hoboken*. Patent No. 426,396, 1890, Stop Watch.

SCHUETZ, C., *Newark*. Patent No. 296,631, 1884, Watch Case, and Patent No. 319,907, 1885, Watch case.

SOUTH BEND WATCH COMPANY. See American National Watch Company.

STANDARD. Model of the New York Standard Watch Company.

THOMPSON, W. H., *Bridgeton*. Watch paper.

TRENTON WATCH COMPANY, *Chambersburg* (now Trenton). Formed from the remains of the New Haven Watch Company in 1885–86. In 1888, it was estimated that the capacity of the factory was 500 watches per day.

The factory in Chambersburg, the main office was in Trenton, was not a building adapted for watch manufacture, but expressly built for that purpose. As was told,* it was so modern that each workman had a window to himself.

To build the factory and help finance the reorganization of the company, investors of Trenton raised $50,000. This increased the capital of the company to a total of $250,000. The new Board of Directors and Officers were J. H. Brewer, T. W. Burger, L. Farrell, J. L. Murphy, W. S. Stryker, W. F. Van Camp, and S. K. Wilson. The officers were President, Brewer; Treasurer, Van Camp; and Secretary, J. C. Thomas.

The Trenton Watch Company failed in 1907, a depression year, and was bought by the firm of Robert H. Ingersoll & Brother.

The Trenton watch was an 18 Size, jeweled movement, stem wound and set. Unusual for the time, the company also made the Silverine cases for their watches.

---

*Henry G. Abbott, "The Watch Factories of America Past and Present."

Two models of the well-made watches of the Trenton Watch
Company.

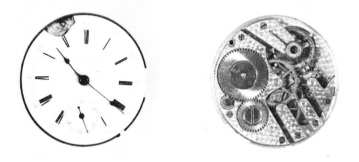

The dial of this watch is marked "Fortuna U.S.A." The "T. W. Co. U.S.A." that otherwise identifies the watch is presumed to be for the Trenton Watch Company of Chambersburg, now part of Trenton. The movement is No. 2,076,537. Courtesy of James W. Gibbs of Philadelphia.

Ingersoll-Trenton watch No. 3,332,316 in a gold-filled "10 year guaranty" case. Courtesy of James W. Gibbs of Philadelphia.

UNITED STATES WATCH COMPANY, *Marion.* (Now part of Jersey City). Not to be confused with the U.S. Watch Company of Waltham, Massachusetts in 1884.

A new factory was erected to accommodate this venture of the United States Watch Company. Organized in 1864 (twenty years before the use of the same name at Waltham) by the firm of Giles, Wales & Co. of New York City. In its beginning only 20 watches per day were made and 200 people employed. By 1871, 400 employees were turning out 100 watches a day.

One of the men employed was a James H. Gerry who, along with other machinists, was from the Waltham Watch Factory and hired to set up the machinery, making what needed to be made. This same James H. Gerry was the inventor, holding Patent No. 236,017, December 28, 1880, for an ingenious winding attachment for a clock. (See Gerry, James H. in Clock Section) Gerry also held Patent No. 235,999, 1882, for a Watch Plate.

"In 1866 the village of Marion was founded, and the United States Watch Company was established there. The company erected a large iron and glass building for the manufacture of watches, and also dwellings for the accommodation of the workmen. At this place, 600 hands were employed producing 150 watches a day of 56 different styles and valued at $11,500. The watch was equal in mechanism and finish to any made in America."—From *History of New Jersey* by J. R. Sypher and E. A. Apgar, p 236. Lippincott, 1870.

In 1872 the United States Watch Company failed and was reorganized in 1873 under the name of Marion Watch Comany.

VINEBURG, E. M., *Englewood.* Watch paper.

WADSWORTH, A., *Newark.* Patent No. 55,750, 1866, Watch, and Patent No. 67,823, 1867, Stem Winding Attachment for Watch.

Arthur Wadsworth was associated in a managerial position with the Newark Watch Company in the technical department. He designed the first model made, the first stem wind model was named "The Arthur Wadsworth" after the inventor. See Newark Watch Company.

WHEELER & SON, *Salem.* Watch Paper.

THE UNITED STATES WATCH CO.'S FACTORY, MARION,
N. J.—GILES, WALES & CO.

Factory of the United States Watch Company.

263

Watch of United States Watch Company. The Edwin Rollo
Model No. 65051, patented March 8, 1870. Gold or gold-filled
hunting case. Courtesy of James W. Gibbs of Philadelphia.

Watch having Marion Watch Company on dial, and United States
Watch Company on back plate. In an 18-kt. gold hunting case.
Courtesy of James W. Gibbs of Philadelphia.

Watch of United States Watch Company, Fayette Stratton Model
No. 162,273. Giles patent, March 13, 1866. Courtesy of James W.
Gibbs of Philadelphia.

Watch of United States Watch Company, J. W. Deacon Model
No. 91,850. Patented March 13, 1866. Courtesy of James W.
Gibbs of Philadelphia.

Watch of United States Watch
Company, Edwin Rollo Model
No. 6868. Patented March 13,
1866. Fahys ore, silver case.
Courtesy of James W. Gibbs of
Philadelphia.

Watch of United States Watch
Company, G. A. Read Model.
Patented March 13, 1866. Dial
with reverse numbers and original
glass back case of factory make.
May be presumed to have been a
sample for the use of salesmen.
Courtesy of James W. Gibbs of
Philadelphia.

Watch of United States Watch
Company, George Channing
Model No. 3951. Giles patent,
March 13, 1866. Silveroid open-
face case. Courtesy of James W.
Gibbs of Philadelphia.

New Jersey Watch Papers

NEW JERSEY WATCH PAPERS. The use of watch papers prevailed among New Jersey watchmakers (repairmen) as elsewhere. The papers, now collectors items in themselves, may still be found in some of the old watches.

Great care was given in the making of the old watchcases to protect the movement. Two cases were actually used. The inner case, into which the movement was set, had as its front a bezel containing the glass which protected the dial and through which the dial could be seen. In the back of this inner case was an aperture through which the key, to wind the watch, was inserted. This inner case then had an outer one which protected the whole, in a mechanical sense, and where the winding aperture had no shield, gave protection against dust and dirt entering the movement.

Between the two cases is where watch papers were placed. Though fitting well there was still some looseness that permitted a rattle and an abrasion between the cases. The insertion of a circular piece of paper or cloth, acting as padding, prevented this. This functional use of the watch paper soon combined with other uses, that of a sentimental reminder and as an area for advertising of repairmen and merchants.

The papers found in watches, imported or brought over by their owners from England, gave Americans an example they followed. Watch papers first appeared in English watches about 1730–1750. In America the first known was in 1757, when the printer, Hugh Gaines, on Queen Street in New York City produced watch papers and advertised, "A beautiful print in miniature of that truly great patriot, the Honorable Mr. Pitt, adapted for watches..." These were offered at six pence each.

We have used the term "papers" to embrace all the circular shaped bits of padding between the two cases of a pair cased watch or inside the back cover of a watch case. In actuality these were also made of linen, silk, and even very thin leather, frequently em-

271

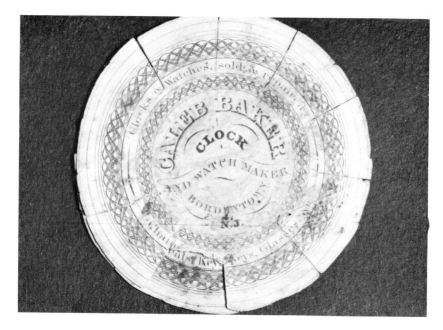

Watch paper of Caleb Baker of Bordentown.

Watch paper of David A. Clark of Trenton.

Watch paper of J. W. Cortelyou of New Brunswick. Placed between two contemporary bank notes to compare the identical engravings on each. Engravings of early watch papers were of very high caliber.

Watch paper of J. Giles of Trenton.

Watch paper of Henry B. James of Mount Holly.

Watch paper of W. H. Thompson of Bridgeton.

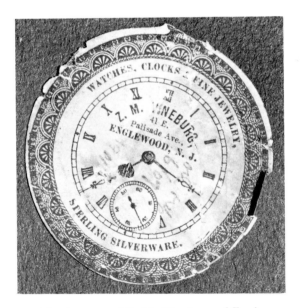

Watch paper of Z. M. Vineburg of Englewood.

Watch paper of Bacon Ware of Salem.

Watch paper of Wheeler and Son of Salem.

broidered with consummate skill, tiny stitches spelling out undying love and/or imperishable devotion along with exquisite ornamentation. Too, the engraver's art was evidenced on these tiny papers. Examples can be seen (see illustrations) where identical engravings appear on a watch paper and on a bank note. The quality of the engraving and printing on the older watch papers were very superior, those in later years became relatively inferior.

As mentioned above, watch papers have been and still are sought by collectors. Their age, craftsmanship, and evidence of the activities and even emotions touch the sensibilities. They are occasionally found inscribed with philosophical lore and with poetry. The poetry frequently reminding the reader of the brevity of his life span. Almost all the writers are unknown. One exception is the paper on which the lines of poetry are attributed to Byron. It was distributed by T. Humphreys, of Barnard Castle, England:

> "Could our tempers move like this machine,
> Not urged by passion nor delayed by spleen,
> And true to Nature's regulatory power
> By virtuous acts, distinguish every hour.
> Then health and joy would follow, as they ought,
> The laws of motion and the laws of thought;
> Sweet health to pass the moments o'er,
> And everlasting joy when time shall be no more."

Much of the information in the above discussion of New Jersey watch papers is from an article by Jean Louis Roehrich, Horological Editor of *National Jeweler* magazine.

Bibliography

Abbott, Henry G.: *The Watch Factories of America*, The Adams Brown Company.

American Horologist and Jeweler magazine, Roberts Publishing Company, Denver, Colorado.

Antiques magazine, New York.

Archives of the State of New Jersey, Trenton, New Jersey.

Baille, G. H.: *Watchmakers and Clockmakers of the World*, N. A. G. Press, Ltd., London, 1951.

Bedini, Silvio: *Early American Scientific Instruments and Their Makers*, Smithsonian Institution, 1964.

Brearley, Harry C.: Time Telling Through The Ages, Doubleday, Page & Co., 1919.

Britten, F. J. (Eds, G. H. Baille, C. Clutton, and C. A. Ilbert: *Old Clocks and Watches and Their Makers*, Seventh Edition, E. and F. N. Spon Ltd., London, 1956.

Bulletin of The National Association of Watch and Clock Collectors, Columbia, Pa.

Chandlee, Edward E.: *Six Quaker Clockmakers*, The Historical Society of Pennsylvania, 1943.

Drepperd, Carl W.: *American Clocks and Clockmakers*, Doubleday and Company, Inc., Garden City, New York, 1947.

Eckhardt, George H.: *Pennsylvania Clocks and Clockmakers*, The Devin-Adair Co., 1955.

Elizabeth Illustrated, The Daily Journal, Elizabeth, New Jersey, 1889.

Gordon, Thomas F.: *History and Gazetteer of New Jersey*.

Historic Elizabeth 1664–1914, Elizabeth Daily Journal, Elizabeth, New Jersey, 1932.

Horner, William S.: *This Old Monmouth of Ours*, Moreau Bros., 1932.

Horology, The National Magazine for Advancement of Timekeeping, now incorporated with *The American Horologist and Jeweler*, Roberts Publishing Co.

How to Obtain Information from United States Patents, Patent Office, U. S. Department of Commerce, Washington, D. C.

Hutchinson, E. T.: "Isaac Brokaw, Jersey Clockmaker," *Proceedings of the New Jersey Historical Society*, July 1954.

Kirkbride's New Jersey Business Directory, 1850–1851.

Littel, John: *Family Records or Genealogies of the First Settlers of Passaic Valley (and Vicinity) Above Chatham—With Their Ancesters and Descendents, as Far as Can be Ascertained*, Stationers Hall Press, Feltville, New Jersey, 1851.

Lloyd, H. Alan: *Old Clocks*, Ernest Been, Ltd., London, 1958.

Local Names and Municipalities, New Jersey State Highway Department, Bureau of Planning and Traffic, Trenton, New Jersey.

Milham, Willis I.: *Time and Timekeepers*, The Macmillan Company, New York, 1947.

Mockridge, Ella W.: *Our Mendham*, Edwards Brothers, Inc., Ann Arbor, Michigan.

Moore, N. Hudson: *Old Clock Book*, Tudor Publishing Company, 1911.

Municipal Incorporations of the State of New Jersey, According to Counties. Department of the Treasury, Division of Local Government, Trenton, New Jersey, December 1, 1958.

Myer, William Starr: *The Story of New Jersey*, Lewis Historical Publishing Company, Inc., New York.

Newark City Directory.

Nutting, Wallace: *The Clock Book*, Old American Co., Framingham, Mass, 1924.

Palmer, Brooks: *The Book of American Clocks*, The Macmillan Company, New York, 1950.

Piaget, H. F.: *The Watch*, private printing, 1868.

Scannell, J. J., (editor and publisher): *New Jersey's First Citizens*, 1917–1918.

Stackhouse, A. M.: Some Genealogical Notes of the Hollinshead Family.

Steware, Frank H.: *Notes on Old Gloucester County*, 1934.

Thayer, Theodore: *As We Were—The Story of Old Elizabethtown*, The Grassman Publishing Company, Inc., Elizabeth, New Jersey, 1964.

United States Patent Office Files, Washington, D. C.

Wenham, Edward: *Old Clocks for Modern Use*, G. Bell & Sons, Ltd., London, 1951.

White, Margaret E.: *Decorative Arts of Early New Jersey*, Volume 25 of The New Jersey Historical Series, D. Van Nostrand Company, Inc., Princeton, New Jersey, 1964.

White, Margaret E.: *Early Furniture Made in New Jersey*, The Newark Museum, Newark, New Jersey, 1959.

Williams, Carl: *Silversmiths of New Jersey 1700–1825*, George S. MacManus Co., Philadelphia, 1949.

Glossary of Clock Terms

ARCH. The curved part of any part of the clock, i.e. arched door, dial, or pediment.

BASE. Sometimes referred to as plinth, when it is the nethermost part of a column. The lower, wider part of the case.

BOSS. The round swelling part of the dial in the lunette portion, sometimes called the medallion. It is upon this, when found, that the clockmaker inscribed his name, the location in which the clock was made, and sometimes the date.

BROKEN PEDIMENT. Generally called the broken arch.

CHAPTER RING. The circular band that contains the numbers for the hours and minutes of the day, or the seconds of the minute. Occasionally a chapter ring was employed by the clockmaker to indicate the days of the month.

CHEEK. The short board inside and at the top of either side of the case giving support to the seat board and determining the proper positioning of the clock within the case.

CORNICE. Topmost moulding on the case of the clock. The kind of moulding usually found here is termed "cavetto." The same style is found at the junction of the trunk and the base of the case.

DENTICKS OR DENTILS. The small rectangular blocks, when seen, just under the cornice of the case. See case of the Brokaw clock.

DIAL FRAME. The door in the hood framing the dial and containing the glass that protects it.

ESCUTCHEON. The decorative piece, usually brass but sometimes ivory, that trims off a keyhole.

FALSE PLATE. Sometimes called the intermediate plate. It is located between the dial and the front plate of the movement. It was provided by the dial maker and offered the opportunity to the clock maker to fit a factory-made dial to a custom-made movement.

FINIAL. A finishing point. Found on many kinds of cabinet work. On clock cases they are usually of brass and often wood. Shapes are defined as ball and spike, urn, acorn, eagles, and flower baskets.

PARTS OF THE CLOCK

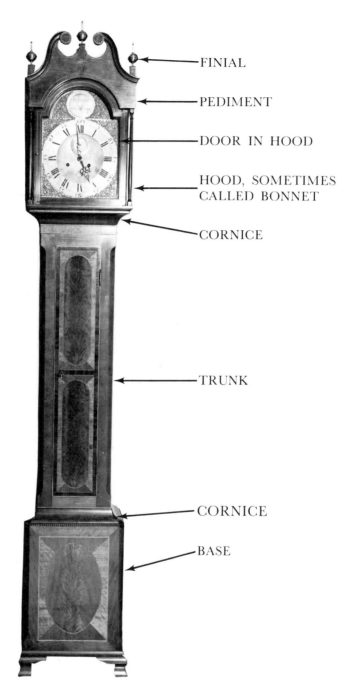

FINIAL

PEDIMENT

DOOR IN HOOD

HOOD, SOMETIMES
CALLED BONNET

CORNICE

TRUNK

CORNICE

BASE

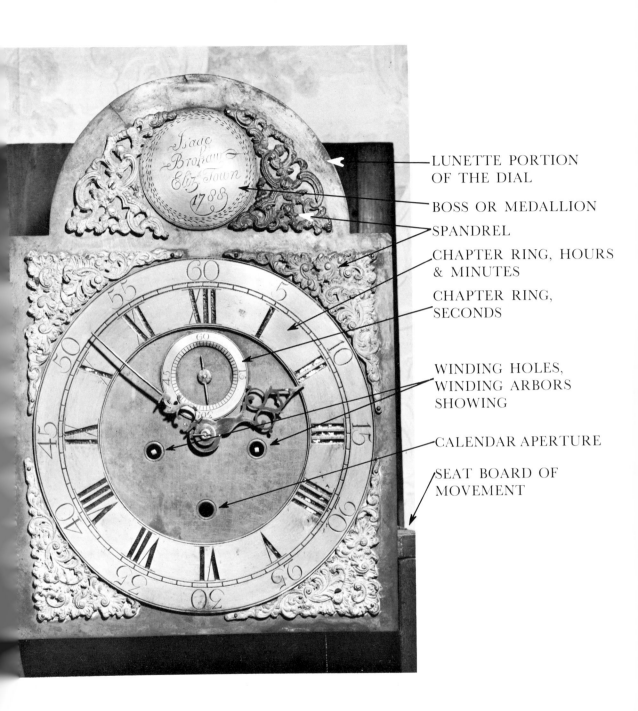

LUNETTE PORTION
OF THE DIAL

BOSS OR MEDALLION

SPANDREL

CHAPTER RING, HOURS
& MINUTES

CHAPTER RING,
SECONDS

WINDING HOLES,
WINDING ARBORS
SHOWING

CALENDAR APERTURE

SEAT BOARD OF
MOVEMENT

FLUTING OR FLUTED. The grooves found in the columns of the hood. Also found in the sometimes found quarter columns in the trunk and/or base. In the hand crafted cases, it has often been found that the number of grooves in one column will not match in number the grooves in the other. Too, the fluting is not always completed around the entire circumference of the columns.

GRANDFATHER CLOCK. A colloquial expression, dating from the title of a once popular song "My Grandfather's Clock." The almost universal acceptance of this popularized nomenclature, in place of the more accurate terminology of long case clock, tall clock, or floor clock. As frequently occurs, when colloquialisms are used, confusion prevails over clarity. In this instance, using the term "Grandfather Clock," it becomes necessary to differentiate between that and Grandmother clock.

GRANDMOTHER CLOCK. A "short" grandfather clock. The word short and/or long are of course relative terms. No clear cut line has yet been drawn where for instance a tall grandmother clock ends and a short grandfather clock begins. Reference to other writings discloses that the difference in size between the two is arbitrary with the individual. This writer elects to call a long case clock that is between 3 and 5 feet in height (if he must) a grandmother clock. There are also those miniatures that are in perfect proportion but about 30 to 36 inches in height that are safer and more appropriately put on a shelf and thereby become a shelf clock.

HOOD. The uppermost part of the case that covers the dial and mechanism. On all New Jersey made clocks they slide forward to be removed. Some very early European clock cases were so made that the hood needed to be lifted up over the dial and mechanism.

LUNETTE. The semicircular top of a dial, above the square portion. Usually the lunette is all of one piece with the dial, infrequently it is a separate section, attached to the lower square part of the dial. The reasons for the use of a lunette are threefold. It gives a more pleasing appearence to the dial, affording more room for embellishment in engraving or painting. It conceals the bell mounted above the movement. It provides an area for the ornamental and functional moon phase mechanism where that exists.

PEDIMENT. A term, when applied to clock cases, designating the frontal part of the hood above the cornice.

PENDULUM APERTURE. The glazed opening in the door of the case through which the swinging pendulum can be seen.

SEAT BOARD. The short board, about 18 inches long by 5 inches wide, upon which the clock movement is mounted. It spans the area between the cheeks (not visible from the outside) in the case.

SPANDREL. The ornamental pieces found on most dials and located in the corners of the dial and in the lunette. They are Arabesque in design with those in the lunette most often not matching those in the dial proper. They are found to be of pewter, lead, or brass.

TRUNK. The body of the case. That part of the case between the base and the hood.

Index